**GLENN'S
MARINE
SERIES**

McCULLOCH

OUTBOARD MOTOR REPAIR AND TUNE-UP GUIDE

FULLY ILLUSTRATED

HAROLD T. GLENN

A COWLES BOOK

Other Books by Harold T. Glenn
Youth at the Wheel
Safe Living
Automechanics
Glenn's Auto Troubleshooting Guide
Glenn's Triumph Repair and Tune-Up Guide
Exploring Power Mechanics
Glenn's Alfa Romeo Repair and Tune-Up Guide
Glenn's Austin, Austin-Healey Repair and Tune-Up Guide
Automobile Engine Rebuilding and Maintenance
Glenn's Sunbeam-Hillman Repair and Tune-Up Guide
Glenn's MG, Morris, and Magnette Repair and Tune-Up Guide
Glenn's Volkswagen Repair and Tune-Up Guide
Glenn's Volkswagen Repair and Tune-Up Guide (Spanish Edition)
Glenn's Mercedes-Benz Repair and Tune-Up Guide
Glenn's Foreign Carburetors and Electrical Systems Guide
Glenn's Renault Repair and Tune-Up Guide
Glenn's Jaguar Repair and Tune-Up Guide
Automobile Power Accessories
Glenn's Volvo Repair and Tune-Up Guide
Glenn's Peugeot Repair and Tune-Up Guide
Glenn's Auto Repair Manual
Glenn's Foreign Car Repair Manual
Glenn's Fiat Repair and Tune-Up Guide
Automotive Smog Control Manual
Honda Repair and Tune-Up Guide

FOREWORD

This is a comprehensive repair and tune-up manual for outboard motors. It is designed to be used as a classroom text or mechanic's reference book, or it can be used by a boating enthusiast who is interested in keeping his engine in tip-top shape. A quick-starting and dependable engine can contribute to an enjoyable vacation; a balky engine can spoil the fun.

This manual is organized about the conventional units of the outboard motor: the engine and the lower unit. Chapters are devoted to servicing the fuel and electrical systems. A separate chapter on engine tuning will enable the enthusiast to get all of the power from the engine that it was designed to deliver. A chapter on maintenance provides vital nontechnical information for fuel mixing and lubricating the units properly, to keep the engine operating dependably.

The first chapter deals with troubleshooting. It enables a mechanic to isolate trouble before beginning to disassemble the mechanism. It helps to pinpoint the trouble so that a mechanic will know what to look for as the unit is being disassembled. This feature can save valuable time when making repairs.

This book contains comprehensive and accurate specification tables, wiring diagrams, and exploded views of all mechanical and electrical units.

A special feature of this book is the use of many step-by-step illustrated instructions for representative types of carburetors, engines, and lower units. The illustrations and text are so closely correlated that no legends are needed. The illustrations have been especially treated to drop out the backgrounds.

The author wishes to thank Messrs. Will Rush, Jack Carroll, Don Lideen, Bob Allman, and Paul Taylor for their kind assistance in helping to take the pictures and for furnishing technical information that has been used in this Guide.

Especial thanks are due my wife, ANNA GLENN, for her devoted assistance in proofreading the text.

Harold T. Glenn

TABLE OF CONTENTS

1 TROUBLESHOOTING

Fuel system troubleshooting — 1
Troubleshooting chart — 2
    Fuel system troubleshooting chart — 3
Ignition troubleshooting — 4
    Ignition system troubleshooting chart — 4
Compression — 5
    Compression troubleshooting chart — 6
Rough operation — 6
    Rough operation troubleshooting chart — 7
High fuel consumption — 8
    High fuel consumption troubleshooting chart — 8
Noises — 8
    Noise troubleshooting chart — 8
Mechanical problems — 9
    Mechanical troubleshooting chart — 9
    Cooling system troubleshooting chart — 9
Electrical system troubles — 10
    Battery troubleshooting chart — 10
    Ignition system troubleshooting chart — 10
    Starting motor troubleshooting chart — 10
Troubleshooting the cranking motor — 11
    Starter-generator troubleshooting chart — 11
    Cranking motor troubleshooting chart — 11

2 MAINTENANCE

Boat performance and propeller selection — 15
    Boat speed — 15
    Center of gravity — 15
    Tilt angle — 15
    Transom height — 15
    Condition of boat bottom — 15
    Propeller selection — 16
    Fuel consumption — 17
Installing the propeller — 17
Tilt pin adjustment — 17
Cavitation — 18
Caution for shallow water operation — 18
Performance factors — 18
Fuel mixing procedure — 19
    Fuel mixing chart — 19
Water pump operation — 20
Stopping — 20
Removing the engine from the boat — 21
Maintenance — 21
    Lubrication — 21
    Fuel filter — 21
    Lubrication chart — 22

Operating in salt water or silt — 23
    After submersion — 24
    Storage — 24
    Using a cleaner — 24
Water wisdom — 25
    Coast Guard regulations — 25
    Rules of the waterways — 25
    Signposts — 25
Seamanship for safety — 25
    Stepping into the boat — 25
    Casting off — 25
    Weather signals — 26
    Rough water — 26
    Danger zone — 26
    Overtaking — 27
    Turns — 27
    Reverse gear — 27
    Skiing — 27
    Stopping — 28
    Docking — 28

3 TUNING FOR PERFORMANCE

General ignition service procedures — 29
    Spark plugs — 29
        Spark plug troubles — 31
        Spark plug protectors — 33
Magneto service procedures — 33
    Removing the flywheel — 33
    Breaker point service — 33
    Breaker point synchronization — 34
    Ignition timing — 34
    Tune-up specifications — 35
    Carburetor throttle pickup adjustment — 36
One-cylinder tune-up service procedures;
3.5 and 4 HP engines — 36
    Breaker point service — 36
    Carburetor adjustments — 37
Two-cylinder engine tune-up service procedures;
7.5, 9, and 12/14 Hp engines — 37
    Breaker point service — 39
    Carburetor-timing synchronous adjustment — 39
    Carburetor adjustments — 39
Two-cylinder engine tune-up service procedures;
25/28 Hp engines — 40
    Breaker point service — 40
    Carburetor-timing synchronous adjustment — 41
        Neutral speed limit adjustment — 41
    Carburetor adjustments — 41

CONTENTS

Two-cylinder tune-up service procedures;

  40–45 Hp engines   41

  Vacuum and throttle switch adjustments   42

  Shift-limit switch   43

  Ignition service procedures   43

  Maximum spark advance adjustment   45

  Carburetor-timing synchronous adjustment   46

  Vacuum lift-off choke   50

  Carburetor adjustments   50

    High-speed adjustment   50

    Altitude trimmer   51

Three-cylinder engine tune-up service procedures;

  75 Hp engine   51

  Shift-limit switch   51

  Distributor service   52

  Carburetor-timing synchronous adjustment   53

  Carburetor adjustments   55

    Altitude trimmer   55

4 FUEL SYSTEM SERVICE

Fuel pump   56

  Fuel pump operation   56

  Fuel pump pressure test   56

  Fuel pump specifications   56

  Fuel pump, R&R   57

  Fuel tank maintenance   57

  Storage   57

Walbro carburetors   57

Walbro carburetor with an adjustable

  high-speed jet; 3.5, 4, and 14 Hp engines   57

  Theory of operation   57

Overhauling a Walbro carburetor with

  an adjustable high-speed jet   58

  Disassembling   58

  Cleaning and inspecting   59

  Assembling   59

Walbro carburetor with a fixed high-speed jet;

  28, 45 (since 1968), and 75 Hp engine   61

  Theory of operation   61

    Idle operation   61

    Mid-range operation   62

    High-speed operation   62

Overhauling a Walbro carburetor with

  a fixed high-speed jet   63

  Disassembling   63

  Cleaning and inspecting   63

  Assembling   64

Marvel-Schebler carburetors   66

Marvel-Schebler, type VHD, carburetor;

  45 Hp engine   66

    Idle operation   66

    Intermediate operation   67

    High-speed operation   67

    Economizer system   67

    Accelerating system   68

Overhauling a Marvel-Schebler,

  type VHD, carburetor   68

  Disassembling   68

  Cleaning and inspecting   71

  Assembling   71

Marvel-Schebler, type SUM;

  7.5 and 9 Hp engines   75

Overhauling a Marvel-Schebler,

  type SUM, carburetor   75

  Disassembling   75

  Cleaning and inspecting   77

  Assembling   77

5 ENGINE SERVICE

Principles of operation   80

Engine details   81

  General instructions   82

Mechanical engine specifications   83

  Disassembling   83

  Cleaning and inspecting   88

  Assembling   91

Overhauling a two-cylinder, 7.5 and 9 Hp engine   100

  Disassembling   100

  Cleaning and inspecting   104

  Assembling   107

75, 45, 28, 14, and 3.5 engine service notes   117

75 and 45 Hp engine service notes   117

28 Hp engine service notes   119

14 Hp engine service notes   121

3.5 Hp engine service notes   123

6 SERVICING THE LOWER UNIT

Description   124

Service procedures   125

One-cylinder engine   125

  Disassembling   125

  Cleaning and inspecting   126

  Assembling   127

Two-cylinder engine   128

  Disassembling   128

  Cleaning and inspecting   131

  Assembling   132

  12 and 14 Hp lower unit   137

  25 and 28 Hp lower unit   138

  40, 43, 45, 60 and 75 Hp lower unit   139

7 ELECTRICAL SYSTEM SERVICE

Cranking motors   140

Overhauling a Delco-Remy cranking motor   140

  Disassembling   140

  Cleaning and inspecting   140

  Assembling   141

CONTENTS

Overhauling a Prestolite cranking motor 142
   Disassembling 142
   Cleaning and inspecting 142
   Assembling 143
Starter-generator; 7.5 and 9 Hp engines 143
   Normal starting 143
   Charging 143
   Start button depressed accidentally 144
Starter-generator troubleshooting 145
   Battery service 145
Electrical tests 145
Starter-generator service 148
   Output test 148
   Solenoid output test 148

Solenoid energizing test 148
   Diode test 149
Starter-generator, R&R 149
   Cleaning and inspecting 150
     Brush holders and field windings 150
     Armature 151
     Diodes 151
   Assembling 151
Alternator 152
   Alternator tests 152
   28 and 45 Hp engine wiring diagram 153
   Selenium rectifier tests 154
   75 Hp engine wiring diagram 154

1
TROUBLESHOOTING

When the engine won't start, it is very important to be able to run through an organized procedure in order to pinpoint the cause of the trouble. Basically, starting troubles can be localized to either the fuel system or the ignition system. After isolating the trouble to the defective system, go through the following suggested check list to determine the exact cause.

FUEL SYSTEM TROUBLESHOOTING

First make sure that there is gasoline in the tank. Sometimes the fuel supply burns up faster than you realize. On engines with a remote fuel tank, make sure that the air vent screw on the fuel tank cap is open, and then squeeze the priming bulb in the fuel line. When the carburetor float bowl is full of gasoline, pressure will be felt on the priming bulb. However, it is possible to force fuel past the needle and seat by additional pressure so that gasoline will flow out of the carburetor throat. *CAUTION: The fuel will leak onto parts of the engine and could cause a fire.* Make sure that all the gasoline is dried up before attempting to start the engine again.

If the carburetor float bowl is dry, check the line for an obstruction. Do this by disconnecting the fuel line from the engine quick-disconnect fitting, and then depressing the check valve in the fuel line connection. Squeeze the bulb and fuel should come out of the line, if it is not obstructed.

If the fuel line to the engine is clear, the trouble could be in the line to the fuel pump or to the carburetor, usually at the fuel line strainer. To check this out, disconnect the fuel line at the carburetor and see if you can force fuel through it by squeezing the priming bulb. *CAUTION: When disconnecting a fuel line, use the proper wrenches, never a pair of pliers. CAUTION: When replacing a fuel line, don't tighten the nuts too much, especially on aluminum castings where the threads can be stripped rather easily.*

Remove a spark plug to check its condition. A wet spark plug means that the engine has been overchoked; a dry spark plug means that no fuel is reaching the combustion chamber. If the carburetor fuel bowl is full, but the spark plug is dry, the carburetor jets may be plugged.

If the spark plug is wet, go through the procedure for starting a flooded engine. Disconnect the fuel line or shut off the fuel supply completely, and then spin the flywheel several times to remove the excess fuel from the combustion chambers. Reconnect the fuel line, replace the spark plug, and then start the engine in the normal manner.

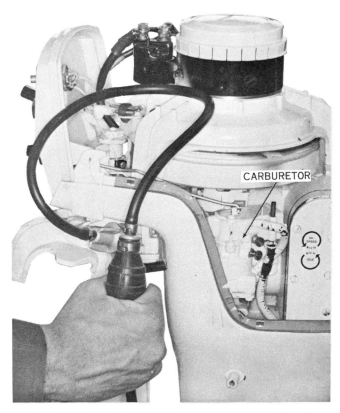

A primer bulb is used to lift fuel from a remote gas tank in order to prime the carburetor. If the carburetor runs out of fuel, the fuel pump may be defective, but the engine can be run by using the primer bulb as a fuel pump.

TROUBLESHOOTING CHART

SYMPTOMS

POSSIBLE CAUSES

Engine does not start	Engine runs irregularly or misses	Engine starts and then cuts out	Engine does not idle properly	Engine speed is faster than normal	Engine speed is slower than normal	Boat speed below normal	Engine overheats	POSSIBLE CAUSES
●		●						FUEL TANK EMPTY
●	●	●			●	●		FUEL FILTER NEEDS CLEANING
	●		●					CARBURETOR LOW-SPEED MIXTURE OUT OF ADJUSTMENT
	●				●	●	●	CARBURETOR HIGH-SPEED MIXTURE OUT OF ADJUSTMENT
					●	●	●	WRONG OIL IN FUEL MIXTURE
	●				●	●	●	WRONG GASOLINE IN FUEL MIXTURE
					●	●	●	NOT ENOUGH OIL IN FUEL MIXTURE
	●		●		●	●	●	TOO MUCH OIL IN FUEL MIXTURE
●								MOTOR FLOODED
●	●		●		●	●		SPARK PLUGS FOULED OR DEFECTIVE
	●		●		●	●	●	WRONG TYPE SPARK PLUGS
●								NO SPARK
	●	●	●		●	●		WEAK OR INTERMITTENT SPARK
	●	●	●		●	●	●	MAGNETO CONTACT POINTS NEED ATTENTION
●								SPARK PLUG LEADS INTERCHANGED
							●	WATER PUMP DEFECTIVE
					●	●	●	COOLING SYSTEM IN NEED OF CLEANING
				●		●		CAVITATION
				●		●		PROPELLER DAMAGED
						●		TILT ANGLE IMPROPERLY ADJUSTED
				●		●		TRANSOM TOO HIGH
						●		TRANSOM TOO LOW
	●	●				●	●	AIR VENT HOLE IN FUEL CAP CLOGGED

A troubleshooting chart is often helpful to determine the general area in which to look for possible causes of trouble.

IDLE MIXTURE ADJUSTING SCREW

DRAIN VALVE

Some of the one-cylinder engine carburetors have a drain valve, which can be depressed to determine whether or not fuel is flowing to the carburetor. The drain valve should be depressed periodically to drain water and debris accumulations from the bowl.

Check the fuel in the carburetor to see if water has gotten into it by catching a little of the gasoline in the palm of your hand. The water will appear as small beads or bubbles. If you blow on the mixture, the gasoline will evaporate, leaving the water behind.

FUEL SYSTEM TROUBLESHOOTING CHART

1. **No fuel in carburetor**
   1a. Empty gas tank
   1b. Clogged fuel filter
   1c. Restricted vent in gas tank
   1d. Defective fuel pump

The condition of the firing end of a spark plug can be used to determine the condition inside of the combustion chamber. This spark plug is running dry, meaning that the mixture is combustible and that the spark plug is doing its work well.

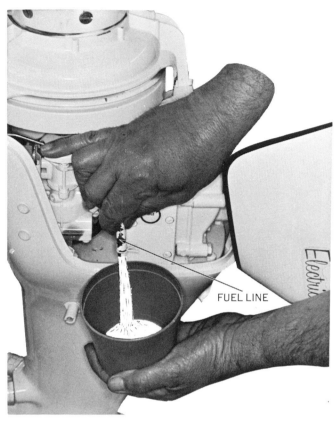

FUEL LINE

To see if the fuel pump is working, disconnect the fuel line and direct its flow into a container. You should be able to determine the condition of the pump before the carburetor fuel bowl runs out of fuel.

   1e. Main adjusting screw closed
   1f. Clogged carburetor screen
   1g. Clogged or broken fuel line
2. **Fuel in carburetor**
   2a. Flooding at carburetor
   2b. Choke not operating
   2c. Water in gasoline
   2d. Restricted carburetor jets
3. **Flooding**
   3a. Choke out of adjustment

The firing end of this spark plug is black with carbon and wet, indicating that the fuel mixture contains too much oil, the fuel mixture is too rich, or the spark plug is not firing.

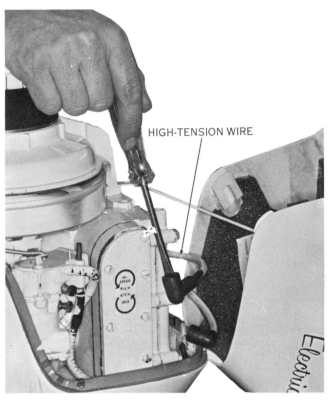

To check the ignition system, hold the high-tension wire about 1/4" away from a metallic surface. Spin the flywheel and a good spark should jump from the wire to ground, if the ignition system is working properly. If the end of the high-tension wire is encased in a boot, as this one is, you can insert a screwdriver tip into the boot to make contact with the wire. Hold the screwdriver so that the shank is about 1/4" away from a good ground to check the spark.

3b. High float level
3c. Float stuck
3d. Excessive fuel pump pressure
3e. Float saturated and not buoyant

IGNITION TROUBLESHOOTING

To check the ignition system, disconnect one of the high-tension wires to a spark plug. Hold the end about 1/4" from the head and spin the flywheel. There should be a good spark from the wire to the metal; otherwise, there is trouble in the ignition system. If there is a spark from the wire to the ground, but the engine does not start because of ignition system defects, then the trouble is generally with the spark plug. Also, if the ignition timing is out of adjustment, the engine will be hard to start.

To check out a spark plug, remove it from the cylinder and connect the high-tension wire to it. Lay the spark plug on the base of the cylinder head, and then

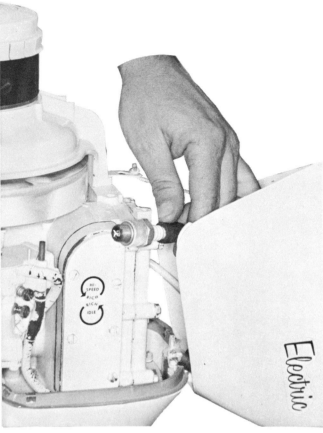

To check out a spark plug, connect the high-tension wire to it and lay the base of the plug on the cylinder head. Spin the flywheel and the spark should jump across the spark plug gap, if the spark plug is good.

spin the flywheel. If there is no spark across the points of the plug, and there was a spark from the high-tension wire to the ground in the preceding test, then the spark plug is shorted. If the plug is good, check the gap and set it to 0.035". *CAUTION: Make the adjustment by bending the outer electrode, never the center one. NOTE: If a gap gauge is not available, you can use two thicknesses of a business card in an emergency.*

IGNITION SYSTEM TROUBLESHOOTING CHART

1. **Spark plugs**
   1a. Fouled
   1b. Wrong type for engine
   1c. Residue on porcelain, especially in salt water areas
   1d. Cracked porcelain
   1e. Loose connections
2. **Ignition coil**
   2a. Weak
   2b. Shorted

CONTACT POINT

This black, pitted breaker point shows evidence of oil on the contact surface, which burned into an insulator. The oil can be placed on the contact point surface with your fingers or by using a dirty feeler gauge to measure the gap.

    2c. Improperly mounted
    2d. Loose wires
  3. **Condenser**
    3a. Weak
    3b. Shorted
    3c. Improperly mounted
    3d. Loose wires
  4. **Breaker points**
    4a. Improperly adjusted
    4b. Pitted or corroded
    4c. Broken or weak spring
    4d. Breaker point loose in its mounting
    4e. Loose wires
    4f. Breaker point arm binding on pivot post, which can cause sluggish action, or the plunger rod can be binding in the bracket
    4g. Broken cam follower or plunger rod
  5. **Wiring**
    5a. Loose, corroded, or poorly soldered connections
    5b. Broken wires (broken under the insulation)
    5c. Oil-soaked wires that cause leaks
    5d. Faulty ground or stop button connection
    5e. Faulty spark suppressors (where used)
  6. **Flywheel**
    6a. Weak magnet

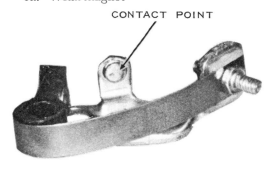

CONTACT POINT

The frosted appearance of this breaker point is an indication that the ignition system was operating properly.

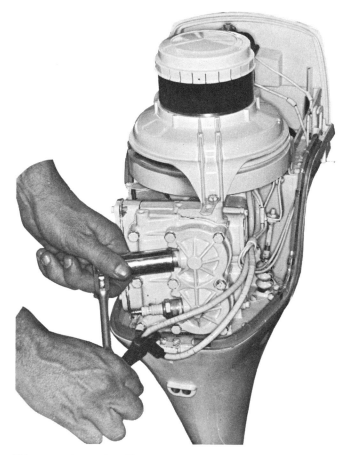

When removing or installing a spark plug, always support the upper end of the socket, or it may tilt and crack the porcelain of the spark plug.

    6b. Cracked magnet
    6c. Improper clearance between magnet pole pieces and coil heels
    6d. Magnet pole pieces sticking or rubbing on coil heels

COMPRESSION

For an engine to start properly, the compression must be good. The amount of compression depends on the ability of the piston rings to keep the gases from escaping. The condition of the cylinder walls, piston ring grooves, and the rings is a factor. Turn the flywheel by hand with the spark plugs installed to check the compression. If compression is present, it can be felt when attempting to complete one revolution of the flywheel. An engine will run with low compression, but it will be difficult to start and certainly won't develop its normal power output. *NOTE: The compression should not vary more than 10 to 15 psi between cylinders.*

COMPRESSION TROUBLESHOOTING CHART

1. **Piston rings**
   1a. Top ring striking ridge in cylinder
   1b. Worn ring grooves
   1c. Rings sticking in ring groove
   1d. Insufficient ring tension
   1e. Insufficient gap clearance
   1f. Excessive side clearance in ring groove
   1g. Undersize pistons
   1h. Scored or wavy cylinder walls

2. **Piston(s)**
   2a. Carbon accumulations in head
   2b. Broken piston, skirt, or ring land
   2c. Insufficient clearance at top of ring land
   2d. Out-of-round, tapered, or worn cylinders
   2e. Excessive piston-to-bore clearance
   2f. Inadequate lubrication

3. **Cylinder(s)**
   3a. Inadequate lubrication
   3b. Contaminated or poor oil
   3c. Exhaust ports clogged with carbon
   3d. Incomplete combustion
   3e. Incorrect type of rings
   3f. Improper cylinder wall finish
   3g. Hole in cylinder
   3h. Insufficient ring gap clearance
   3i. Distorted block or crankshaft

ROUGH OPERATION

An engine that is not operating smoothly can have trouble in the ignition or the fuel system. Closely allied with the fuel system is trouble with a reed valve which affects the fuel distribution to two cylinders of a multi-cylinder engine.

To check the ignition system, disconnect a spark plug wire, and then run the engine at its rough-operating point. Note the size of the spark that jumps from the wire to the terminal of the spark plug. Widen the gap to see if the spark becomes intermittent as the gap increases. This is a rather rough test, but it can be used to throw some light on the condition of the ignition system.

If the trouble is in the fuel system, it can be checked by changing the air-fuel ratio and noting its effect on the running of the engine. For example, with the engine running at its rough-operating point, close the choke valve slowly and note the effect that enriching the mixture has on the operation of the engine. If the engine smooths out with the choke valve partially closed, then the air-fuel mixture is too lean. The lean condition can be

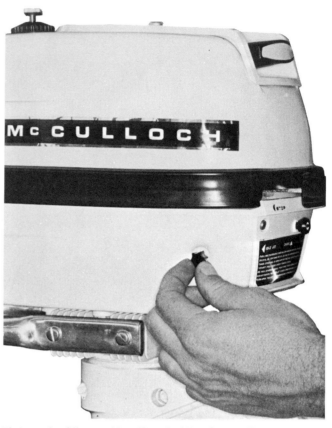

If the engine idles roughly, adjust the idle mixture adjusting screw to see if you can smooth out the idle. Turning the screw to the right (clockwise) leans the mixture. The high-speed adjusting screw at the base of the carburetor can be adjusted in a similar manner.

caused by a poor carburetor mixture adjustment or by dirt in one of the jets.

If the engine is running too rich, enriching the air-fuel mixture with the choke will cause the engine to slow down and run even rougher.

If the engine is running too rich, the trouble could be a leaking fuel pump diaphragm, which will allow raw fuel to enter the crankcase and mix with the carbureted fuel. This condition can be suspected if one carburetor of a multi-cylinder engine is running excessively rich. The trouble can be isolated further by removing the spark plugs to check their condition. A wet spark plug indicates an excessively rich mixture.

A defective reed valve will cause the engine to spit back through the carburetor air intake. In some cases, white smoke will come out of the carburetor throat. Hold your hand over the air intake and you may be able to feel raw gasoline being returned through the throat of the carburetor.

On a multi-cylinder engine, one reed valve block controls the air-fuel mixture of one carburetor, which may feed two cylinders. Remove the spark plugs of these two cylinders to determine which one is wet in order to pinpoint the defective reed valve.

ROUGH OPERATION
TROUBLESHOOTING CHART

1. **Engine misfires because of ignition troubles**
   - 1a. Incorrect spark plug gap
   - 1b. Defective or loose spark plugs
   - 1c. Spark plugs of an incorrect heat range
   - 1d. Sticking breaker arm
   - 1e. Incorrect breaker point gap
   - 1f. Breaker points not synchronized
   - 1g. Loose wire in primary circuit
   - 1h. Defective distributor rotor
   - 1i. Corroded or pitted breaker points
   - 1j. Cracked distributor cap
   - 1k. Leaking or broken high-tension wires
   - 1l. Weak armature magnet
   - 1m. Worn cam lobes on the distributor or magneto shaft
   - 1n. Worn distributor or magneto shaft bushings
   - 1o. Defective coil or condenser
   - 1p. Defective ignition switch
   - 1q. Spark timing out of adjustment
2. **Engine misfires because of fuel troubles**
   - 2a. Dirt or water in fuel
   - 2b. Reed valve stuck open or broken
   - 2c. Incorrect fuel level
   - 2d. Carburetor loose at flange
   - 2e. Throttle valve not closing completely
   - 2f. Throttle valve turned to one side or incorrectly positioned
3. **Engine misfires at high speeds**
   - 3a. Weak breaker arm spring
   - 3b. Defective coil
   - 3c. Coil shorts through insulation
   - 3d. Breaker points improperly adjusted
   - 3e. Poor breaker point contact
   - 3f. Spark plug gap set too wide
   - 3g. Too much spark advance
   - 3h. Wrong type of spark plugs
   - 3i. Excessive carbon in cylinders
   - 3j. Poor compression
   - 3k. Dirty carburetor
   - 3l. Lean carburetor adjustment
   - 3m. Crankcase magneto adaptor flange worn out-of-round
4. **Engine backfires through the exhaust**
   - 4a. Cracked spark plug porcelain
   - 4b. Carbon track in distributor cap
   - 4c. Crossed spark plug wires
   - 4d. Air leak at intake deflector
   - 4e. Improper ignition timing
5. **Engine backfires through the carburetor**
   - 5a. Poor quality fuel
   - 5b. Air-fuel mixture too lean
   - 5c. Excessively lean or too rich a fuel mixture
   - 5d. Improper ignition timing

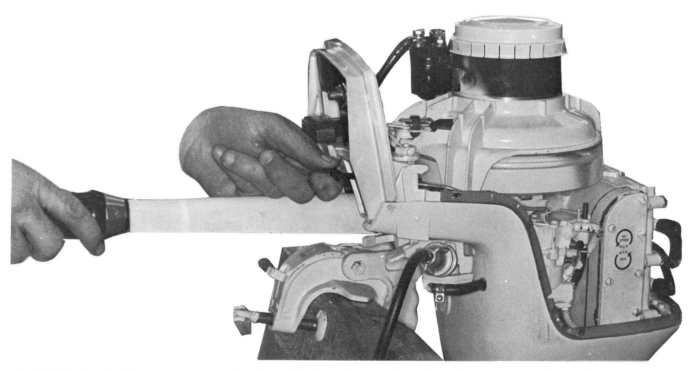

To check the air-fuel mixture, close the choke valve slowly while the engine is running at its rough-operating point. If the engine smooths out with the choke valve partially closed, then the air-fuel mixture is too lean.

    5e. Pre-ignition
    5f. Improperly seated or a broken reed valve
    5g. Improperly adjusted carburetor

6. **Pre-ignition**
    6a. Spark advanced too far
    6b. Incorrect type of spark plugs
    6c. Burned spark plug electrodes
    6d. Incorrect breaker point setting
    6e. Excessive oil in fuel
    6f. Poor grade of fuel
    6g. Lean carburetor mixture
    6h. Excessive engine temperature
    6i. Carbon deposits in combustion chamber

HIGH FUEL CONSUMPTION

Excessively high fuel consumption is generally caused by carburetor defects. However, the efficient operation of the ignition system is essential for good utilization of the fuel that is drawn into the engine. To this extent, defects in the ignition system will cause the fuel consumption to increase.

HIGH FUEL CONSUMPTION TROUBLESHOOTING CHART

1. **Carburetor troubles**
    1a. Cracked carburetor casting
    1b. Leaking fuel line connection
    1c. Defective carburetor bowl gasket
    1d. Warped or bent bowl cover
    1e. Plugged vent hole in cover
    1f. High float level
    1g. Loose float needle valve seat
    1h. Defective needle valve seat gasket
    1i. Worn needle valve and seat
    1j. Ridge worn in lip of float
    1k. Worn float pin or bracket
    1l. Float binding in bowl
    1m. Choke lever stuck
2. **Fuel pump troubles**
    2a. Leaking around diaphragm cover
    2b. Leaking fuel pump diaphragm
    2c. Warped check valves
    2d. Dirt or sediment in valves
    2e. Corroded valve seats
    2f. High fuel pump pressure
    2g. Leakage at lines and connections
    2h. Leaking gas tank
    2i. Leakage at filler cap
3. **Ignition conditions**
    3a. Retarded spark timing

    3b. Leaking high-tension wires
    3c. Incorrect spark plug gap
    3d. Fouled spark plugs
    3e. Worn breaker points
    3f. Faulty spark advance adjustment
    3g. Defective condenser
    2h. Weak ignition coil
    3i. Pre-ignition
4. **Compression troubles**
    4a. Worn or broken piston rings
    4b. Worn pistons or cylinders
5. **Miscellaneous troubles**
    5a. Loose carburetor flange
    5b. Improperly adjusted or worn throttle linkage
    5c. Restricted exhaust system
    5d. Carbon in manifold
    5e. Overheating engine
    5f. Use of poor grade of gasoline
    5g. Sticking reed valve
    5h. Poorly seated reed valve

NOISES

Checking engine noises is one of the more difficult troubleshooting procedures because noises travel in the metal of the engine and sometimes appear to be coming from every part. However, it is possible to localize noises by using a stethoscope or a listening rod.

NOISE TROUBLESHOOTING CHART

1. **Knocking in powerhead**
    1a. Loose flywheel
    1b. Excessive bearing clearance
    1c. Spark advanced too far
    1d. Pre-ignition
    1e. Excessive end play in crankshaft
    1f. Out-of-round bearing journals
    1g. Bent or twisted crankshaft
    1h. Broken crankshaft
2. **Knocking from the connecting rods**
    2a. Excessive bearing clearance
    2b. Worn connecting rod
    2c. Misaligned connecting rods and cap
    2d. Bent or twisted connecting rod
    2e. Worn crankshaft journal
3. **Center main bearing noises**
    3a. Improperly installed main bearing
    3b. Crankshaft striking the reed stops
4. **Piston noises**
    4a. Excessive piston-to-cylinder bore clearance

4b. Out-of-round cylinder
4c. Loose piston pin
4d. Carbon in the top of the cylinder
4e. Piston pin bent
4f. Excessive clearance at the ring grooves
4g. Broken piston ring

5. **Gear housing noises**
5a. Propeller shaft worn or sprung
5b. Bearing worn
5c. Broken gears
5d. Propeller hub rubbing against the gear case cover
5e. Improperly fitted gears
5f. Worn gears
5g. Wrong conical angle
5h. Incorrect backlash
5i. Oil seal leakage
5j. Water in gear housing
5k. No grease in gear housing

MECHANICAL PROBLEMS

Generally, mechanical problems in an engine require it to be disassembled to correct the condition. The following Mechanical Troubleshooting Chart will assist in determining the possible causes of mechanical troubles.

MECHANICAL TROUBLESHOOTING CHART

1. **Reed valve breakage**
   1a. Improper valve opening
   1b. Corrosion of reed valve
   1c. Poor valve seat

2. **Excessive bearing wear caused by dirt**
   2a. Careless service methods
   2b. Contaminated oil

3. **Bearing wear caused by improper fitting**
   3a. Distorted connecting rods
   3b. Mixed connecting rod caps
   3c. Dirt between bearing and connecting rod bore
   3d. Out-of-round, tapered, or worn journal
   3e. Warped crankshaft or block
   3f. Excessive crankshaft end play
   3g. Scored bearing surface
   3h. Improper clearance
   3i. Use of wrong service tools

4. **Bearing failure caused by corrosion**
   4a. Overheating
   4b. Storage in damp place
   4c. Water entering powerhead

5. **Bearing failure caused by improper operation**
   5a. Overspeeding
   5b. Spark detonation
   5c. Improper engine break-in
   5d. Racing a cold engine
   5e. Using the wrong type or grade of oil
   5f. Using an improper fuel
   5g. Improper spark timing

6. **Bearing wear caused by lubrication problems**
   6a. Excessive engine temperatures
   6b. Insufficient engine warm-up time
   6c. Insufficient quantity of oil

7. **Engine speed faster than normal**
   7a. Cavitation
   7b. Transom too high
   7c. Propeller hub slipping
   7d. Wrong propeller pitch

8. **Engine speed slower than normal**
   8a. Carburetor out of adjustment
   8b. Too much oil in fuel mixture
   8c. Wrong oil in fuel
   8d. Wrong type of gasoline
   8e. Spark plugs fouled
   8f. Wrong type of spark plugs
   8g. Tilt angle not correctly adjusted
   8h. Transom too high
   8i. Transom too low
   8j. Cavitation
   8k. Weeds tangled on gear housing
   8l. Propeller damaged
   8m. Wrong propeller pitch

COOLING SYSTEM TROUBLESHOOTING CHART

1. **Overheating with an external leak**
   1a. Loose cylinder block cover bolts
   1b. Damaged cylinder block cover gasket
   1c. Warped cylinder block cover or block
   1d. Cracked cylinder wall
   1e. Porosity of cylinder head

2. **Overheating without a leak**
   2a. Incorrect ignition timing
   2b. Improper fuel mixture
   2c. Improperly adjusted spark advance linkage
   2d. Defective spark advance linkage
   2e. Pre-ignition

3. **Overheating caused by restricted circulation**
   3a. Pump impeller loose on shaft
   3b. Water inlet pipe seal ring not in place
   3c. Pump blades broken or worn
   3d. Water pump worn

3e.   Clogged water jacket passages
3f.   Water tube mislocated
3g.   Water tube cracked or corroded
3h.   Cover not securely tightened

ELECTRICAL SYSTEM TROUBLES

The battery supplies the current required to crank the engine. On engines with a distributor-type ignition system, the battery furnishes the current to energize this circuit. Some engines are equipped with an alternator to charge the battery. In the absence of an alternator, the battery must be charged by an outside source.

It takes specialized testing equipment and knowledge of its use to determine accurately the condition of an electrical unit. However, the following troubleshooting charts can be used for guidance in tracing out some types of electrical troubles.

BATTERY TROUBLESHOOTING CHART

1. **If frequent charging is required**
   1a.   Corroded battery terminals
   1b.   Alternator grounded or shorted
   1c.   Worn-out or inefficient battery
   1d.   Rectifier defective
   1e.   Short in charging circuit
   1f.   Excessive use of electrical units
   1g.   Short circuit in ignition switch
2. **Battery does not take a charge**
   2a.   Low water level
   2b.   Worn-out battery
   2c.   Cracked case
   2d.   Spilled electrolyte
   2e.   Internal short circuit
   2f.   Impure electrolyte
3. **High water loss**
   3a.   Too high a charging rate
   3b.   Old or inefficient battery
   3c.   Leaking battery cell
   3d.   Worn-out battery
   3e.   Cracked case
   3f.   Defective current regulation

IGNITION SYSTEM TROUBLESHOOTING CHART

1. **Oxidized breaker points**
   1a.   High charging voltage

1b.   Resistor of incorrect value
1c.   High resistance in condenser circuit
1d.   Incorrect type of ignition coil

2. **Ignition coil failures**
   2a.   Extremely high voltage
   2b.   Moisture formation
   2c.   Excessive heat from engine
3. **Spark plug troubles**
   3a.   Incorrect type of spark plug
   3b.   Too rich a fuel mixture
   3c.   Incorrect oil mixture
   3d.   Inferior grade of gasoline or oil used
   3e.   Overheated engine
   3f.   Too much carbon in combustion chamber
   3g.   Improper torque on spark plug

STARTING MOTOR TROUBLESHOOTING CHART

1. **Starter fails to crank engine**
   1a.   Poor battery ground
   1b.   Jammed or broken drive
   1c.   Broken teeth on flywheel
   1d.   Grounded switch
   1e.   Solenoid shorted or open circuited
   1f.   Burned contact points in switch
   1g.   Improperly seated brushes
   1h.   High mica between commutator segments
   1i.   Shorted armature
   1j.   Shorted field or brushes
2. **Excessive current draw**
   2a.   Broken or jammed starter drive
   2b.   Dirty or gummed armature
   2c.   Shorted armature
   2d.   Grounded armature or field
   2e.   Misaligned starting motor
   2f.   Worn armature shaft bearings
   2g.   Misaligned armature shaft
   2h.   Loose field pole pieces
   2i.   Engine turns hard
3. **Burned commutator bars**
   3a.   Excessive arcing at brushes
   3b.   Excessive voltage
   3c.   Improperly seated brushes
   3d.   Open-circuited armature coils
   3e.   Open field circuit
   3f.   Weak brush spring tension
4. **Excessive noise**
   4a.   Defective starter drive
   4b.   Chipped or broken flywheel teeth
   4c.   Insufficient lubrication
   4d.   Worn armature shaft bearings

CRANKING MOTOR TROUBLESHOOTING CHART

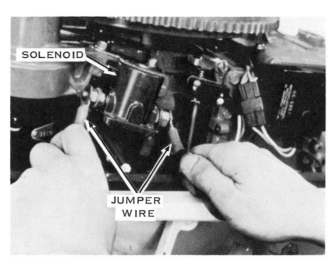

Cranking motor troubles can be caused by a defective solenoid. To check out the solenoid, use a jumper wire to bridge the heavy contact terminals. This bypasses the solenoid entirely, and the cranking motor should work unless there are other troubles in the circuit. CAUTION: Use a heavy piece of wire as a jumper, or the wire will get hot and could burn your hands.

4e. Misaligned starting motor
4f. Loose starter mounting
4g. Sprung armature shaft

TROUBLESHOOTING THE CRANKING MOTOR

When a cranking motor does not turn, or doesn't crank the engine, the electrical system must be checked with an accurate voltmeter and ammeter to determine the source of trouble. Use a 0–15 voltmeter and a 0–500 ammeter. The following chart is keyed to the illustration to give a useful step-by-step tracing procedure.

STARTER-GENERATOR TROUBLESHOOTING CHART

1. **Starter-generator operates erratically when the START button is depressed.**
   1a. Battery weak or dead
   1b. Loose or improper battery connections at the front panel or battery terminals
   1c. Starter-generator field defective
   1d. Worn, broken, or damaged brushes
   1e. Incorrect brush spring tension
   1f. Short in armature windings
   1g. Dirty or defective commutator
2. **Starter-generator does not function when the START button is depressed.**
   2a. Failure in start button circuit

STEP NUMBER	METER READINGS (In Volts)			CAUSE
	As Hooked Up	With Starter Button Pushed	If It Reads	
V-1	12	10–11	12 / Below 10	Open Circuit / Weak Battery
V-2	12	0–1	Over 1 / Below 8	Loose Terminal Open Circuit / High-Resistance
V-3	0	1/2–1	Below 1	Loose Terminal Broken Wire
V-4	0	1/2–1	Over 1	Loose Terminal
V-5	0	1/2–1	Over 1	Loose Connection Corroded Connection
V-6	12	1/2–1	Over 1	Defective Solenoid
V-7	12	1/2–1	Over 1	Loose Terminal
V-8	0	0	Over 0	Poor Ground
A-9 ①	0	125	Well Over 125	Defective Cranking Motor

① An ammeter of this capacity must use a shunt. **Caution: Do not connect a small ammeter in this circuit, or you will burn it out.**

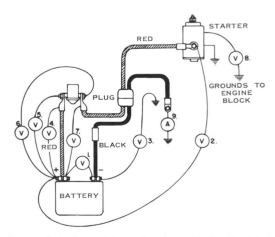

This diagram is to be used in conjunction with the Troubleshooting Chart to make accurate tests, which will determine the exact area of trouble.

    2b. Loose or damaged connections

    2c. Weak or dead battery

    2d. Incorrect brush spring tension

    2e. Brushes not contacting commutator surface properly

    2f. Damaged commutator

3. Weak or dead battery

    3a. Worn or defective brushes

    3b. Dirty or defective commutator

    3c. Loose connection at insulated brush or grounded field coil windings

    3d. Defective armature

    3e. Defective diode

    3f. Overloaded battery caused by excessive use of radio or lamps

To check the generator, disconnect the main generator lead from the solenoid terminal and connect it to the ammeter lead. Connect the other ammeter lead to the main battery lead. Start the engine with the rope starter and check the charging rate, which should be 3–8 amperes at 4,200–5,500 rpm. CAUTION: Don't use the electric starter to crank the engine, or you will burn out the ammeter.

A smooth-running, dependable engine ensures a good time.

These engines are designed for a transom height of 15″ for the smaller sizes and 20″ for engines of 30 Hp or over.

To install the engine on the transom, open the boat bracket clamp screws, and then install the unit, centering it with respect to the keel or centerline of the boat. Observe the position of the anti-cavitation plate with respect to the keel. The plate must be level with or slightly below the keel or bottom of the boat. If the anti-cavitation plate is more than one inch below the bottom of the boat, shim the engine, using 1/4″ strips of hard wood between the top of the transom and the boat brackets, as shown.

Installation of the engine on the transom should be given very careful attention. The clamp bracket not only must support the weight, but is subject to thrust, impact, inertia, and steering stresses. These forces are applied directly to the transom through the clamp bracket assembly. Therefore, to avoid damage to the transom and to prevent the engine from working loose during opera-

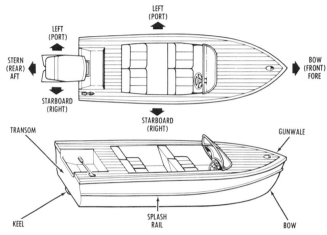

In this book, specific names are used to refer to the various sides of the boat and motor. These names are an accepted standard in the marine industry, and their usage remains the same regardless of the direction from which the boat is viewed.

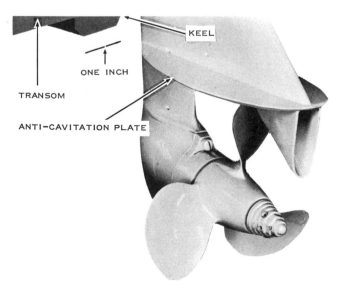

The anti-cavitation plate should be level with or slightly below the bottom of the boat when the engine is properly mounted.

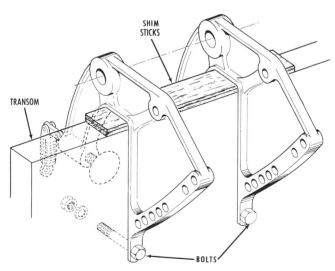

Shim sticks should be used under the motor mounting brackets if the anti-cavitation plate is more than 1″ below the bottom of the boat.

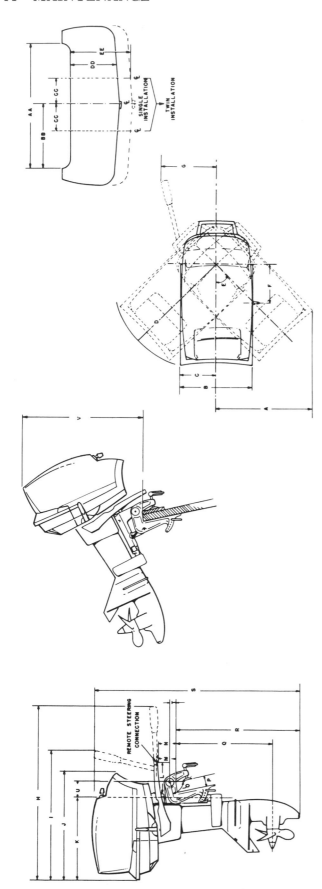

MOUNTING DIMENSION CHART

MODEL	OBC. CERT. H.P.	A	B	C	D	E	F	G	H	I	J	K	L	M	N	O	P	Q	R	S	T	U	V	AA		BB		CC		DD		EE	
																								S	T	S	T	S	T	S	T	S	T
12	14.1	13-1/2	11-1/2	5-3/4	11-1/2	45°	2	8-1/4	29-1/2	22	21	15	7	3	1-3/4	70°	2	21	25-1/2	41	1-9/32	4-1/4		20	40	10	20	-	10	-	15	-	-
28	*28	15-1/2	13	6-1/2	17-1/2	45°	3-1/2	8-1/2	37-1/2	27	25	16-3/4	8-3/4	4-1/4	2-1/2	70°	2-1/4	22	27-1/4	44-1/2	1-1/16	4-7/8	29"	24	46	12	23	-	12	-	15	-	-
28	*28LS	15-1/2	13	6-1/2	17-1/2	45°	3-1/2	8-1/2	37-1/	27	25	16-3/4	8-3/4	4-1/4	2-1/2	70°	2-1/4	27	32-1/4	49-1/2	1-1/16	4-7/8	29"	24	46	12	23	-	12	-	15	-	20
45	*45	17-1/2	17-1/4	8-5/8	20-1/2	40°	3-1/2	-	-	-	27-1/4	19	9	4	3-1/4	70°	2-1/4	24	25-1/2	48	1-1/16	5	23½	30	58	15	26	-	12½	-	15	-	-
45	*45LS	17-1/2	17-1/4	8-5/8	20-1/2	40°	3-1/2	-	-	-	27-1/4	19	9	4	3-1/4	70°	2-1/4	29	34-1/2	53	1-1/16	5	23½"	30	58	15	26	-	12½	-	15	-	20
75	75.2	17-1/2	17-1/4	8-5/8	20-1/2	40°	3-1/2	-	-	-	27-1/4	19	9	4	3-1/4	70°	2-1/4	24	30	49-1/2	1-1/16	5	31"	30	58	15	26	-	12½	-	15	-	-
75	75.LS	17-1/2	17-1/4	8-5/8	20-1/2	40°	3-1/2	-	-	-	27-1/4	19	9	4	3-1/4	70°	2-1/4	29	35	54-1/2	1-1/16	5	31"	30	58	15	26	-	12½	-	-	-	20

*Manual and Electric Starting Models
**Extended Shaft Models

NOTE:
1. The "F" dimension will appear on opposite side in the case of 1963 45 H.P. and 75 H.P. motors.
2. The "M" and "N" dimensions will vary with motor tilt.

This chart shows the operating clearances and mounting dimensions for the various outboard motors made by this manufacturer.

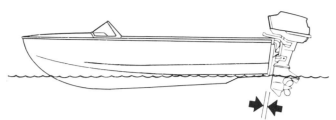

INSUFFICIENT ANGLE, BOW DIGS

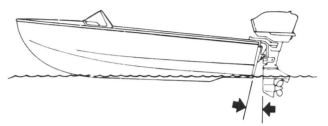

CORRECT ANGLE, TOP PERFORMANCE

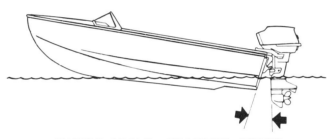

EXCESS ANGLE, TRANSOM DRAGS

For best performance, the tilt angle should be adjusted so that the engine is vertical to the surface of the water. If the lower unit is tilted out too far, the bow of the boat will ride too high. If the lower unit is tilted too close to the transom, the bow will plow, or dig into the water. NOTE: Changes in boat loading may require a change in the tilt angle.

tion, it is important that the clamp screws are tightened securely and equally and that the larger engines are secured to the transom with bolts through the brackets. *CAUTION: Failure to bolt the engine to the transom may result in damage to the boat and/or loss of the engine.* Apply a waterproof sealant to the bolts to prevent water from reaching the wood core of the transom. During operation, the clamp screws should be checked occasionally for tightness.

BOAT PERFORMANCE AND PROPELLER SELECTION

Many times the engine is blamed for inefficient operation when actually the fault lies with the boat or the installation of the engine on the boat.

Boat Speed

Consult the boat house bulletin charts for similar boat sizes and loading. These boats and engines are run with the best-suited propellers and with an optimum set-up (transom height and tilt angle, usually with an aft position of the center of gravity).

Center of Gravity

For maximum speed, move the weight aft until the boat porpoises or is about to porpoise. This reduces the wetted surface to a minimum. Only the rear half of the boat bottom should be wet.

Tilt Angle

The tilt angle should be set so that the anti-cavitation plate is about parallel to the bottom of the boat. The speed of boats that have the center of gravity located forward may be improved sometimes by tilting the lower unit out one pin hole. This will tend to raise the bow and reduce the wetted surface. If the lower unit is tilted in, the boat will ride with the bow down, wetting more of the bottom and thereby reducing speed.

Transom Height

A greater transom height will increase boat speed, but it makes cavitation more likely. The effect of transom height on speed is slight at speeds between 15–20 mph, but it becomes important at speeds of 30–35 mph and above.

Condition of Boat Bottom

For maximum speed, a boat bottom should be nearly a flat plane where it contacts the water. It should be especially straight and smooth in the fore-and-aft direction. The bottom is said to have a "hook" if it is concave in the fore-and-aft direction when viewed from below. When the boat is planing, this causes more lift on the bottom near the transom and allows the bow to drop, which greatly increases the wetted surface and reduces

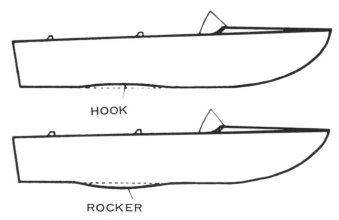

HOOK

ROCKER

For maximum speed, the bottom of the boat should be a flat plane where it contacts the water. A boat bottom with either a hook or rocker can affect the speed and operation to a large degree.

boat speed. A hook is frequently caused by supporting the boat too far forward to the transom while hauling it on a trailer or during storage. A "rocker" is the reverse of a "hook" and much less common. The boat has a rocker if the bottom is convex in the fore-and-aft direction when viewed from below. A boat with a rocker has a strong tendency to porpoise. Moss, barnacles, or other surface irregularities that increase skin friction of the boat bottom will cause a considerable loss of boat speed. Surface roughness of the gear case, caused by barnacles or corrosion, easily can result in a speed loss of 1 or 2 mph on boats in the 30 to 35 mph and higher class.

PROPELLER SELECTION

The speed at which a given boat will travel is governed mainly by the horsepower available. Use of the correct propeller will allow the engine to turn at the recommended rpm and develop full power. First, select a trial propeller, using the approximate boat length and load, if known. This usually will be the correct choice. Establish the exact transom height and tilt pin setting by test.

To check, make a trial run, using an accurate tachometer. It is important that the engine rpm remain within the recommended limits. The trial run should be made with a light load of one person. Under these conditions, it is desirable to have the engine rpm near the top of the recommended limit so that, under a heavy load, the speed will not fall below recommendations. If

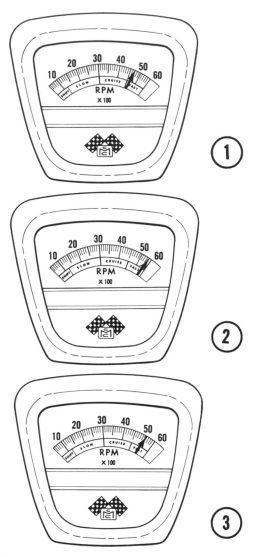

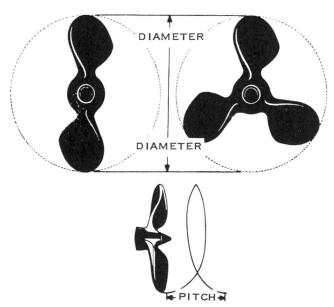

The two basic dimensions of a propeller are pitch and diameter. The pitch is the theoretical distance that a propeller advances if there is no slip. The diameter is the distance from the tip of one blade to the tip of the other.

These three tachometer illustrations show the method of determining the correct propeller for a given engine-boat combination. ① The first trial run, using an 11-1/2″ diameter by 14″ pitch propeller, showed a tachometer reading of 4,700 rpm. The manufacturer's specification for this engine is 4,800–5,400 rpm; therefore, this propeller is loading the engine too much and should be replaced with one having less pitch. ② The second trial run, using a propeller 11-1/2″ diameter by 10″ pitch, shows a tachometer reading of 5,800 rpm, too fast for the load. To correct, increase the pitch. ③ The third trial run, using a propeller 11-1/2″ by 12″ pitch, shows a tachometer reading of 5,100 rpm, safely within the 4,800–5,400 specifications.

the engine rpm is too high, try a higher pitch or the same pitch cupped. Likewise, if the rpm is low, try a lower pitch propeller. There normally is a 300–500 rpm change between propeller pitches.

For dual installation, the next higher pitch propeller may be best. For water skiing, it may be desirable to use the next lower pitch propeller; however, do not operate at full throttle when using a ski propeller and not pulling skiers. *CAUTION: If, in this connection, a propeller has too little pitch for the application, dangerous over-*

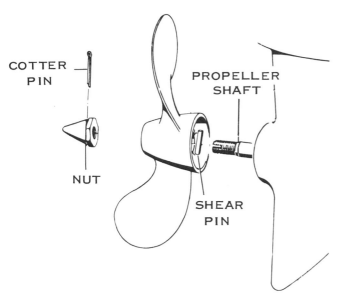

This shows how the propeller is installed for the smaller engines.

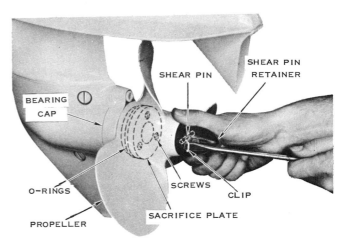

The shear pin for the larger engines is located in the plastic retainer, as shown. The larger engines use a "sacrifice plate" to protect the components from electrolysis in salt water. This plate should be examined every 30 days and replaced if eroded.

speed of the engine will result! If a propeller has too much pitch for the application, acceleration will be slow.

Light, fast boats require higher pitch propellers, while heavier boats require lower pitch propellers. Use aluminum propellers in salt water areas to reduce the electrolytic action that can result in corrosion and pitting of metal surfaces.

FUEL CONSUMPTION

For a planing boat, the maximum miles per gallon is obtained with an engine that will just plane the boat (15–17 mph) at full throttle. Larger engines, or dual engines that will drive the boat faster, will give fewer miles per gallon. A given boat and engine usually will get the most miles per gallon at or near full throttle. An improper carburetor setting can reduce the miles per gallon by 10–15%.

INSTALLING THE PROPELLER

All models are equipped with a shear pin which is designed to break before the engine is damaged. The engine is equipped with a two-position lock which prevents the propeller from rising out of the water when the unit is run in reverse. The same lock can be used to tilt the powerplant all the way forward in order to change a propeller or to replace a sheared drive pin. To raise the engine, release the lock lever and then pull the engine as far forward as possible.

To replace a shear pin, pull the rubber propeller

cap off the propeller shaft. Remove the sheared pin, align the shear pin hole in the propeller hub with the hole in the propeller shaft, insert a new shear pin, and then install the rubber propeller cap.

Extra drive pins and cotter pins are provided in a neoprene holder attached to the recoil starter. If these parts are used, be sure to replace them as soon as possible so that you always have a spare. In an emergency, a suitable piece of wire can be used.

TILT PIN ADJUSTMENT

Holes are provided in the clamp bracket to permit changing the location of the tilt lock pin for proper adjustment of the tilt angle. The tilt angle of the engine should be set so that the anti-cavitation plate is about

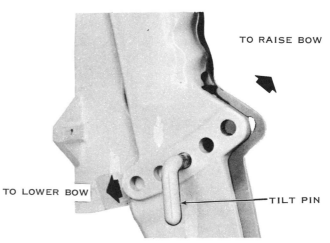

Holes are provided in the clamp bracket to allow you to change the location of the tilt lock pin in order to change the tilt angle of the engine.

parallel with the bottom of the boat. The speed of boats which have the center of gravity located forward may be improved sometimes by tilting the lower unit out one tilt pin hole. This will tend to raise the bow and reduce the amount of wetted surface. If the lower unit is tilted in, the boat will ride with the bow down, wetting more of the bottom and reducing speed. Raising the bow generally will improve operation in rough water.

Under ideal conditions, efficiency will be best with the lower unit operating in a level position, because the entire thrust will then be applied parallel to the plane of motion. With some boats, under certain unfavorable conditions of loading, there will be a tendency to ride stern high or bow high. This condition can be corrected considerably by adjusting the tilt angle so that the boat rides level. Operation with excessive tilt will reduce performance noticeably and may induce cavitation. It is preferable, therefore, to level the boat by proper loading rather than by an extreme adjustment of the tilt angle. Except in very rough water, a properly designed boat will ride level and will plane without porpoising if the tilt angle is correctly adjusted and the boat is favorably loaded. *CAUTION: Do not operate the engine with the tilt lock pin removed.*

CAVITATION

Cavitation is indicated by intermittent or continued overspeed of the engine, accompanied by violent water agitation and a sharp reduction of boat speed. Cavitation occurs when the slip stream (flow of water past the propeller) changes from a smooth, consistent flow to a turbulent one. Under conditions of cavitation, the turbulent area or cavity around the propeller causes a very noticeable loss of forward thrust. Generally, cavitation is caused by one of the following: (1) The propeller's operating too close to the surface. This may be due to the transom's being too high, to an adjustment of the tilt angle that causes the lower unit to be too high, or to the boat's riding stern-high because of improper loading. (2) Turbulence in the slip stream, which can be caused by an obstruction, such as a wide or deep keel.

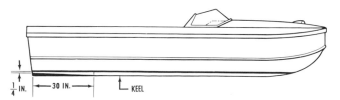

To avoid cavitation, the keel of the boat must be tapered, beginning about 30" forward of the transom, so that it projects no more than 1/4" below the hull at the transom end.

This can be helped in most cases by tapering the keel in both width and depth from a point about 30" forward of the trailing edge; however, for best results, the boat should have no keel in the last 4' of stern. (3) Fouling of the propeller by weeds, rope, etc. (4) Damaged or broken propeller blades. A broken blade is indicated usually by excessive vibration.

CAUTION FOR SHALLOW WATER OPERATION

When the shift lever is in REVERSE, the lower unit is locked in its normal operating position. The shock load of an impact could cause transom breakage, particularly when the boat is backing up. Proceed cautiously when in reverse motion and be careful of underwater obstructions. *CAUTION: Do not accelerate the engine to high speeds or the stern will dip and you may swamp the boat.*

PERFORMANCE FACTORS

Engineers have always known that weather exerts a profound effect on the performance of internal combustion engines. Therefore, all horsepower ratings refer to the power that the engine can produce at its rated speed under a specified set of weather conditions.

Summer conditions of high temperature, low barometric pressure, and high humidity combine to reduce power. Reduced power, in turn, is reflected in decreases in boat speeds—decreases of as much as two or three mph, in some cases. Nothing can restore this loss of speed for the boatman except the coming of cool, dry weather.

To point out the practical consequences of weather: an engine running on a hot, humid summer day may encounter a loss of as much as 14% of the horsepower it can develop on a dry, brisk spring or fall day. The horsepower that an internal combustion engine can produce depends on the density of the air that it is consuming; this density, in turn, depends upon the temperature of the air, its barometric pressure, and its content of water vapor or humidity.

Accompanying this weather-inspired loss of power is a second, more subtle loss. At fitting-out time in early spring, the engine may have been equipped with a propeller which allowed it to turn at its rated speed at full throttle. With the coming of the summer weather and the consequent drop in available horsepower, this propeller will be too large. Hence, the engine will operate at less than its rated speed. Due to the horsepower-speed

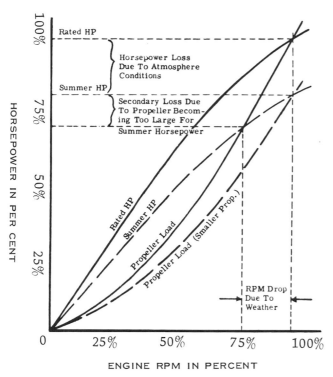

This graph shows how the changes in temperature affect the performance of an engine.

(Graph labels: Rated HP; Horsepower Loss Due To Atmosphere Conditions; Summer HP; Secondary Loss Due To Propeller Becoming Too Large For Summer Horsepower; Rated HP; Summer HP; Propeller Load; Propeller Load (Smaller Prop.); RPM Drop Due To Weather. Y-axis: HORSEPOWER IN PER CENT, 100%, 75%, 50%, 25%. X-axis: ENGINE RPM IN PERCENT, 0, 25%, 50%, 75%, 100%)

McCULLOCH FUEL MIXING CHART

100:1 Fuel Mixture ①

McCulloch 100:1 Outboard Motor Oil	6 Oz.
Gasoline (90 Octane)	5 Gal.

50:1 Fuel Mixture ②

McCulloch 40/50 Outboard Motor Oil	12 Oz.
Gasoline (90 Octane)	5 Gal.

20:1 Fuel Mixture ③ ④

McCulloch 40/50 Outboard Motor Oil	32 Oz.
Gasoline (90 Octane)	5 Gal.

① All models from 1962, except the 3-1/2 Hp models.

② All models, including the 3-1/2 Hp engine from 1963–65.

③ All 3-1/2 Hp models through 1962.

④ Not recommended for engines that use surface-gap spark plugs.

characteristics of an engine, this results in a further loss of horsepower and another decrease in boat speed. This secondary loss can be regained by switching to a smaller-pitch propeller which will allow the engine to run at its rated speed again.

FUEL MIXING PROCEDURE

A marine gasoline, automotive white, and a light aircraft gasoline of 90 octane rating are the only ones recommended for outboard motor use. An outboard motor is extremely sensitive to inconsistent fuel/oil mixing and to fuel mixtures resulting from different brands of gasolines and oils. Such changes often require frequent readjustments of the carburetor.

Mix the oil with the gasoline in the following ratios: Mix a 6 oz. can of 100:1 two-cycle motor oil with each 5 gallons of gasoline. Mix a 12 oz. can of 40/50:1 two-cycle motor oil with each 5 gallons of gasoline. An approved outboard motor oil of SAE 40 weight can be mixed in the ratio of 50:1 by adding 12 ozs. of the oil to 5 gallons of gasoline. *CAUTION: Don't use multi-grade oils or other automotive oils that have a large amount of detergents. Oils which contain metallic additives are exceedingly harmful to two-cycle engines. Their use can result in piston burning and scoring. CAU-*

TION: Using less than the recommended amount of oil will result in very serious engine damage because of insufficient lubrication. Using more than the recommended amount of oil will cause spark plug fouling, erratic engine operation (poor carburetion), excessive carbon accumulation, and smoking.

Always use fresh gasoline; never store gasoline in the fuel tank over an extended period. Cracked gasolines contain ingredients that change into gums when stored for any length of time. These gums and varnish products will cause carburetor troubles and spark plug burning. Always drain the fuel from the gas tank if the engine is to be stored for any length of time.

Mix the fuel in a well-ventilated location, preferably out of doors. *CAUTION: Don't smoke while handling gasoline.* Accurately measure the required amounts of oil and gasoline. Pour the oil into a remote fuel tank, and then add an equal amount of gasoline. Mix thoroughly by shaking vigorously, and then add the balance of gasoline and mix again. *CAUTION: Cleanliness is of prime importance in mixing fuel, as even a very small particle of dirt can cause carburetor trouble.*

Automotive oils are not suitable for outboard motor use, because many of them contain a dilution inhibitor which resists thorough mixing of the oil with gasoline. The resulting separation may put a layer of oil at the bottom of the tank, with gasoline at the top and with various proportions of the mixture between. Since the fuel pick-up tube is located at the bottom of the tank, the engine may receive an excessively high proportion of oil when the tank is full and almost straight gasoline when it is nearly empty. Therefore, at first, the engine may smoke excessively and foul the spark plugs. Later on, it may overheat and score the pistons because of insufficient lubrication.

Automotive oils with metallic detergents are very

Using the wrong oils or an incorrect mixture of oil and gasoline can result in piston scoring. Follow the manufacturer's instructions to protect your outboard motor.

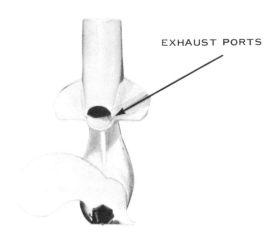

EXHAUST PORTS

The exhaust outlet is below the water line, but it should be checked periodically to be sure that it is clean.

effective in reducing varnish formation and piston ring sticking in a four-cycle engine, where very little of the oil gets into the combustion chamber. But in a two-cycle engine, all of the oil must pass through the combustion area, where the metallic additives form deposits when they come into contact with the hot surfaces of the spark plugs, piston crowns, and combustion chamber. These deposits cause pre-ignition and detonation which result in piston crown burning, piston scuffing, and cylinder wall scoring. If the metallic particles bridge the spark plug gap, the plug will cease to fire.

WATER PUMP OPERATION

Normal operation of the water pump is indicated by a stream of water discharging from the idle relief outlet when the engine is idling. If at any time this stream is not evident, stop the engine immediately and check the hole with a piece of wire to be sure that it is not clogged. This stream indicates that the water pump is operating. *CAUTION: Avoid further operation until the water pump and cooling system have been checked.* Operation of the engine with an inoperative water pump or an obstruction in the cooling system will cause overheating and severe damage.

STOPPING

If the engine is to be ready for an immediate restart, stop by shifting into neutral and depressing the STOP button. If the engine is to remain idle for a period of time or if it is to be removed from the boat, stop it by disconnecting the fuel line and allowing the engine to run at idling speed until it stops of its own accord, indicating that the carburetor is dry. Close the air vent screw on the fuel tank cap.

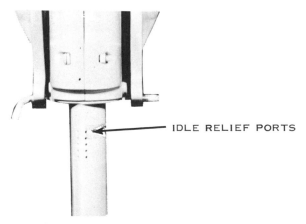

IDLE RELIEF PORTS

With the engine idling, there should be a stream of water discharging from the idle relief holes on the smaller engines.

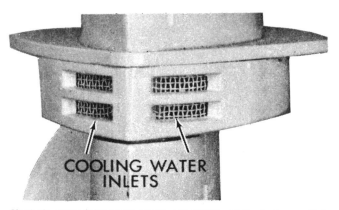

COOLING WATER INLETS

Check the water inlet screen on the one-cylinder engine to be sure that it is free of dirt.

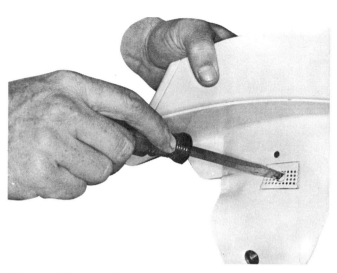

The water inlet screen for the two-cylinder engine is located under the anti-cavitation plate.

REMOVING THE ENGINE FROM THE BOAT

Disconnect the remote controls and steering connections, if so equipped. Disconnect the fuel line. Loosen the clamp screws and detach the safety cable or chain, if so equipped. Keep the engine in an upright position, resting on its skeg, until all water is drained from the driveshaft housing. *CAUTION: If the engine is placed on its side while the water remains trapped in the driveshaft housing, some water may drain into the powerhead and enter the cylinders through the exhaust ports.* Be sure that all water drain holes in the gear housing are open so that the water can drain completely.

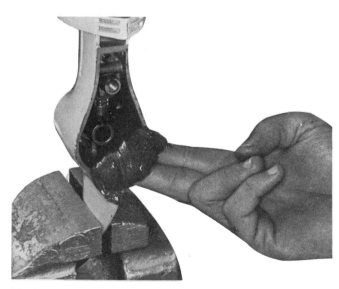

The lower unit of the one-cylinder engine must be packed with grease, as discussed in the text.

MAINTENANCE

Lubrication

The lower gear casing of all but the single-cylinder engine must be drained and refilled monthly to protect the gears and bearings. To drain the gear casing, stand the engine upright, and then remove the vent and filler plugs. Allow the old lubricant to drain out, and then refill the gear casing through the drain opening with the specified amount of EP # 90 Lubricant. Replace the vent and drain plugs, tightening them only as much as necessary to compress the seals properly.

In the single-cylinder engine, the gear case is packed with Shell Darina # 2. The level of the grease should be checked once each month and the gear case should be emptied and refilled once each season. *CAUTION: Don't use EP # 90 in the gear case of the single-cylinder engine.*

Fuel Filter

All of the engines have a fuel filter screen to prevent

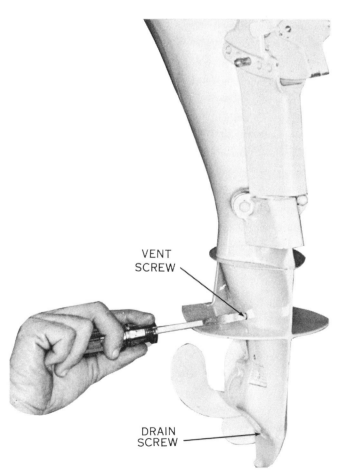

To drain the lubricant from the lower unit, remove the vent and drain plugs.

LUBRICATION CHART

LUBRICANT	APPLICATION	AMOUNT	3.5–4.0	7.5–9.0	14	140 OX	28	45	75
Shell Nerita #3	All grease seals on the OD	Sparingly	●	●	●	●	●		
	Water pump and bailer drive pins	During assembly						●	●
	All lower units parts	During assembly	●	●	●	●	●		
	Lower shift rod and cam	Liberal		●					
	Connecting rod bearings	Liberal	●	●	●	●	●		
	All needle and roller bearings	Liberal						●	●
	Main bearings	Moderate			●	●	●		
	Wrist pin bearings	Moderate		●	●	●	●		
	Water pump seals	During assembly			●	●	●		
Lubriplate #630AA	Stator plate mounting	Liberal	●	●	●	●	●		
	Throttle actuator linkage	Moderate			●	●	●	●	●
	Clamp screws and pads	Moderate	●	●	●	●	●	●	●
	Lower unit bearing	Moderate	●	●	●	●			
	Shift lever shaft	Liberal			●	●	●	●	●
	Shift linkage	Moderate		●					
	Shift limit beam (at detent and pivot)	Moderate					●		
	Twist grip and gears	Moderate			●	●	●		
	Speed control shaft and bearing	Liberal			●	●	●		
	Recoil starter assembly	Liberal	●	●	●	●	●	●	
	Pivot tube bearings	Liberal			●	●	●	●	●
	Throttle shaft	Liberal	●						
	Hood latch assembly	Moderate			●	●	●	●	●
	Water pump cavities	Moderate			●	●	●	●	●
	Thrust tilt linkage	Moderate				●		●	●
	All linkage points	Moderate	●	●	●	●	●	●	●
Moly Sulfide Molub Alloy	Upper driveshaft splines	Liberal	●	●	●	●	●	●	●
Lithium Grease #3	All grease seal lips	Sparingly						●	●
	All grease seals OD	Sparingly						●	●
Motor Oil SAE 20–30	Upper and lower main bearings	Liberal	●						
Hypoid Gear Lubricant EP #90	Lower gear unit case	Fill to vent hole			●	●	●	●	●
Outboard Gear Grease	Lower gear unit case	Pack	●						

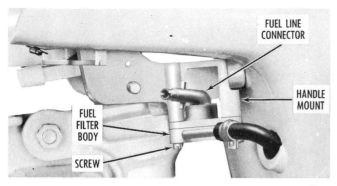

A fuel filter is located on the handle mount base for the 7.5 and 9 Hp engines. It should be removed and cleaned at regular intervals.

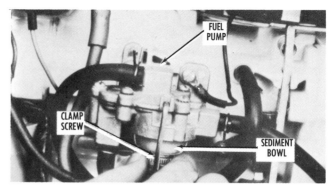

On the larger engines, the fuel filter and sediment bowl should be cleaned regularly.

dirt particles from reaching the carburetor. The filter screen must be cleaned every three months to maintain good performance. The filter is installed in the area of the fuel connector. To remove the screen for cleaning, take out the three screws which secure the filter body to the underside of the handle mount, on the port side. Clean the filter screen, and then reinstall it in the handle mount. *CAUTION: Make sure that the screws which fasten the filter body to the handle mount are tightened firmly and that the O-ring seal in the filter body is in good condition.*

OPERATING IN SALT WATER OR SILT

Operation in salt water or silt results in the accumulation of salt or mineral deposits in the cooling system water passages and around the cylinder water jackets. Unless removed regularly, these deposits will build up to the extent that circulation of the cooling water becomes restricted or cut off entirely. Also, the deposits act as an insulator, reducing the transfer of heat from the cylinders to the water. This loss of transfer will cause overheating, loss of performance, and serious damage.

Even though the interior surfaces of outboards are treated to resist corrosion, there remains a possibility of a mechanical build-up of salt and silt deposits that no form of protective coating can prevent; it can be minimized by occasional flushing with fresh water. While no complete protection for exterior surfaces is known, there are ways in which electrolysis and corrosion damage can be minimized. By following the simple steps below, you can increase materially the life of all exposed parts and decorative finishes.

An outboard motor that is to remain on a boat should be tilted out of the water. Always disconnect the negative battery terminal when in dock or in storage for any period of time.

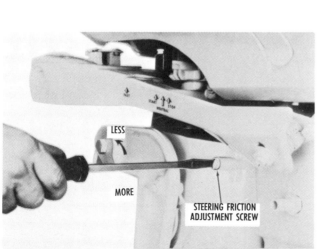

The steering adjustment screws can be tightened to provide the amount of steering friction desired by the operator.

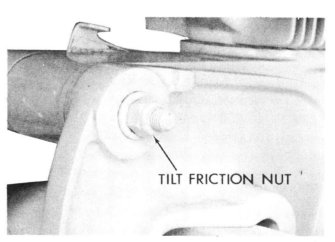

The tilt adjustment is made by tightening a friction nut.

Lubricate the swivel bracket frequently and other moving parts regularly. Grease the thumb screws on the clamps to insure smooth operation. Grease the propeller shaft splines occasionally with a waterproof-type lubricant, thus enabling the propeller to be removed easily.

Spray the entire powerhead with a coating of a rust preventive to protect the finish of all parts beneath the cowl. The exterior of the engine also can be sprayed with rust preventive to keep corrosion from dulling the finish.

Attach a flushing hose and turn on the water tap. Operate the manual starter to facilitate the flow of water through the pump. *CAUTION: Do not use full pressure from a city water tap. CAUTION: During and after flushing, keep the motor in an upright position, resting on the skeg, until all water has been drained from the driveshaft housing in order to prevent water from entering the powerhead through the exhaust ports.*

AFTER SUBMERSION

An engine which has been submerged must be disassembled completely for cleaning and inspecting. This should be done as soon as possible after recovery. Delayed action will encourage rust and corrosion of internal parts. Emergency treatment may be accomplished by following the instructions below. This temporarily will retard rust and corrosion. Basically, the points to remember are these: (1) Recover the engine as quickly as possible. (2) Wash the entire unit with fresh, clean water to remove mud, weeds, etc. (3) Get as much water as possible out of the powerhead. Most of the water can be eliminated by removing the spark plugs and operating the starter with the spark plug holes facing downward. *CAUTION: If the engine does not turn freely when the starter is operated, do not force it. This may be an indication of internal damage, such as a bent connecting rod or a broken piston.* (4) Pour alcohol into the cylinders because it will dissolve water, and then lubricate all the internal parts that are accessible. This can be accomplished by injecting oil into the spark plug holes, installing the spark plugs, and then operating the starter to distribute the oil. If alcohol and oil are not available, insert a rod into the fuel check unit to open the check valve, and then actuate the primer bulb, thus forcing the oil-fuel mixture into the cylinders. (5) Disassemble and clean the engine as soon as possible.

STORAGE

When storing an outboard motor for the winter, be sure that all water drain holes in the gear housing are open and that the flushing plug is removed so that the

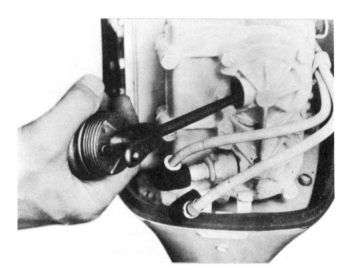

After an engine has been submerged, it is very important to lubricate all internal parts as quickly as possible. To get oil into the cylinders, remove the spark plugs and squirt the oil into the spark plug ports.

water will drain out. Trapped water may freeze and expand, thus cracking the gear housing and/or the water pump housing. Check and refill the lower unit with gear lubricant before storage to protect against possible water leakage into the gear housing, caused by a loose air vent or grease filler plug. Be sure to replace the gaskets under the vent screws.

Prior to packing at the factory, new engines are "fogged out" at the final test by injecting approximately 2 oz. of rust preventive oil through the carburetor air intake. This practice is desirable when engines are stored in a damp place, or when they are expected to stand idle for a long period of time. When an engine is started after fogging, the spark plugs should be checked and replaced, if necessary, as they may have become fouled from the rust preventive oil.

Before storage, disconnect the fuel line or turn off the fuel shut-off valve, and then allow the engine to run at idling speed until it stops of its own accord, indicating that the carburetors are dry. Drain the fuel tank and fuel lines. This will prevent gum from forming in the tank, lines, and carburetor. If an outboard motor is to remain on a boat, it should be tilted out of the water.

USING A CLEANER

Several chemical cleaners have been developed to remove the carbon deposits which reduce the power of an outboard motor. To use the cleaner, run the engine until normal operating temperature is reached. On one- and two-cylinder engines, slowly pour about 10 oz. of the cleaner through the carburetor throat while the engine is running at a fast idle of 1,200 rpm. Use a pump-type oil can or pressure sprayer. Increase the speed and stall the engine with the balance of the cleaner. Let the engine stand for at least 30 minutes. Start the engine and run it at full throttle for 5 minutes.

On three-cylinder models, with the engine operating at its lowest rpm above stalling, feed a sufficient quantity of the cleaner into the throat of one carburetor. Let the engine run until it is firing on all cylinders again, and then repeat the process for the other carburetors. Next, flood the entire engine through all of the carburetors and allow it to stand for 1/2 hour.

To clean a severely carbonized engine, tilt it to a horizontal position and close as many intake and exhaust ports as possible by turning the flywheel so that the pistons cover the ports. Pour the cleaner through the spark plug holes. Let it set overnight, position the engine vertically, and then pull the starter rope several times to remove the excess cleaner. Prepare the engine for running and repeat the regular cleaning process as discussed above.

WATER WISDOM

Coast Guard Regulations

To enjoy the waterways safely, it is advisable to check with authorities in regard to local, state, and federal boating regulations and restrictions. In addition, here are a few suggestions: (1) Carry one approved life jacket or buoyant cushion per person, (2) one approved fire extinguisher, (3) a flashlight or lantern, (4) an anchor, (5) a first aid kit, (6) a compass, (7) an extra propeller, and (8) enough fuel.

Rules of the Waterways

Keep practicing water safety by observing the following simple rules: (1) Do not operate your boat near swimmers, skin-divers, or fishermen. (2) Keep clear of sailing craft and rowboats, yielding the right-of-way to them. (3) Always keep to the right; show respect and courtesy at all times.

Signposts

Know the channel markers to follow a safe and confident course. When returning, keep the red buoys on your right; black buoys on your left. Black-and-white, vertically striped buoys indicate the middle of a channel; always pass as close as possible to them, on either side. Black-and-red, horizontally striped buoys indicate obstruction; give them a wide berth.

SEAMANSHIP FOR SAFETY

Stepping into the Boat

Step into the *center* of the boat. Don't carry equipment aboard; keep your hands free for steadying yourself. Equipment should be placed on the edge of the dock, and then lifted into the boat.

Casting Off

Back away *slowly* in reverse gear.

The outboard motor has opened a new frontier for leisure time activities.

Never carry equipment aboard. Equipment should be placed on the edge of the dock, and then lifted into the boat.

Weather Signals

Any flag or light which is all or part red is a warning that bad weather is developing or exists.

Rough Water

When heading into rough water, *decrease* speed but maintain plane to prevent water from entering the boat. Alter the direction of attack on the waves until it feels right.

Danger Zone

The danger zone is a 112-1/2° arc which is measured from dead ahead to off the starboard, or right-hand, side. A boat *must yield* the right-of-way to any other craft which approaches it within the danger zone.

Always carry enough approved equipment to ensure your safety.

BLACK CAN AND SPAR
BUOYS

RED NUN AND SPAR
BUOYS

OBSTRUCTION
MARKER

MID-CHANNEL
BUOY

Buoys are the signposts of the waterways. When returning, keep the red buoys on your right, black buoys on your left. The black-and-white, vertically striped buoys indicate the middle of the channel; always pass close to them, on either side. The black-and-red horizontally striped buoys indicate obstructions; give them a wide berth.

Overtaking

A boat which is being overtaken has the right-of-way.

Turns

Practice boat turns in order to test for the amount of stern swing of your boat.

Reverse Gear

When reversing, the stern will dip; move your passengers forward to guard against swamping the boat. When reversing, the motor will not tilt up when striking a submerged object; therefore, be alert so that the transom will not be damaged.

Skiing

The recommended procedures are: (1) Check the

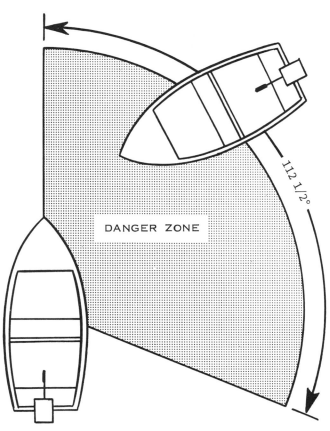

DANGER ZONE

112 1/2°

You must yield the right-of-way to any boat approaching within the danger zone.

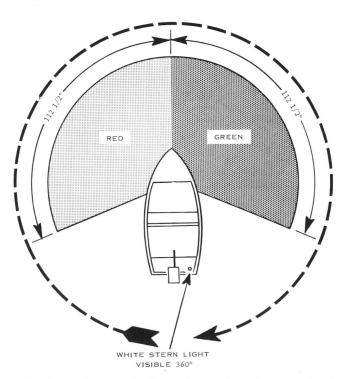

112 1/2°   112 1/2°

RED   GREEN

WHITE STERN LIGHT
VISIBLE 360°

This diagram shows the direction and color of the lights that should be visible when you use the boat at night.

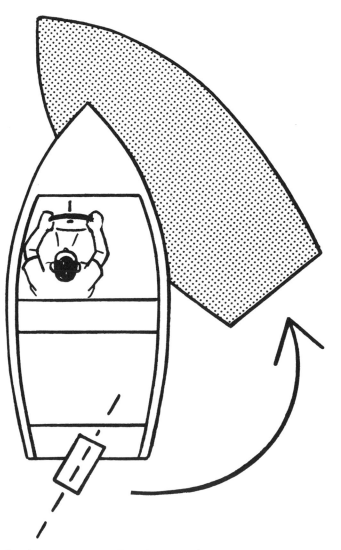

Practice turns to get used to the stern swing so that you can become an expert.

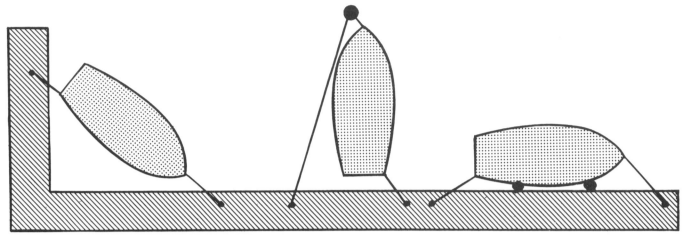

Secure your boat to the dock properly to avoid buffeting by the wind.

equipment for safe, smooth operation. (2) Know the skier's hand signals. (3) Carry an observer in the boat.

Stopping

Practice for stopping distance at various boat speeds in order to be prepared for any unusual situation.

Docking

Approach a dock slowly and, if possible, into the wind, waves, or current. Avoid buffeting by securing the boat to the dock, as shown.

Know the law, and obey it! You'll enjoy your vacation that way.

3

TUNING FOR PERFORMANCE

The material in this chapter is divided into two basic sections, the first of which covers the general service procedures required for servicing all ignition systems. The second section deals with the tuning procedures for each type of engine, according to the number of cylinders and horsepower rating.

Each of the engine-type sections is a complete unit, covering the ignition timing and carburetor adjustments that are necessary to make the engine perform to its designed power potential.

GENERAL IGNITION SERVICE PROCEDURES

SPARK PLUGS

Spark plugs are a small but vitally important component of modern gasoline engines. Without proper spark plug operation, satisfactory engine performance cannot be obtained. Outboard motors are equipped with spark plugs of a special electrode gap design.

Spark plugs are made in a number of heat ranges to satisfy a variety of possible operating conditions. Some types, having a long insulator firing end, transfer heat slowly and are used where combustion chamber temperatures are relatively low. Sustained idling, stop-and-start, and light-load operation produce this condition. The short insulator plug remains cool enough to avoid pre-ignition and excessive gap erosion.

The appearance of spark plugs will indicate whether they are too hot or too cold for the engine. The end of the spark plug is subjected to intense heat from the burning of the fuel mixture, and this heat is dissipated by conduction along the porcelain end of the spark plug and thus to the cylinder jacket. If the porcelain part, which extends into the cylinder, is comparatively long, the heat

cannot be dissipated rapidly, and the spark plug will run hot. If the porcelain is short, the heat can pass through it more quickly, and the spark plug will run cold.

The spark plug which is installed originally in the engine is the one that will give best service under normal operating conditions; however, if the speed is increased by placing the engine on a lighter hull, it may be necessary to substitute a colder spark plug. If the engine is placed on a heavier boat and the speed is decreased, a hotter spark plug may be required. If trouble arises with spark plugs fouling while trolling, changing to a hotter type of spark plug may help.

If the spark plug is operating at its most efficient temperature, the porcelain part, which projects inside of the cylinder, will be dark brown, chestnut, or coffee-

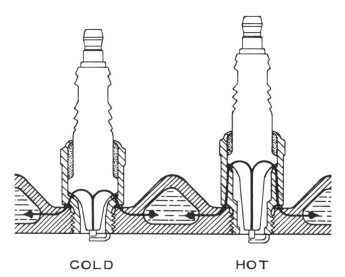

COLD   HOT

The heat range of a spark plug is determined by the length of the heat path from the tip of the insulator to the coolant or, in the case of an air-cooled engine, to the metal of the cylinder head.

Always inspect the firing end of each spark plug as it is removed from the engine. The deposits and coloration tell a story of operating conditions. This is the way that a normal spark plug should look.

OVERHEATING

This spark plug is operating too hot. Either it is of an incorrect heat range, or the engine is running too hot.

CORE BRIDGING

The electrodes are shorted out by core bridging, the result of using the wrong oil.

WET FOULING

Wet fouling can be caused by too much oil in the mixture or by a defective spark plug. This spark plug was not firing.

ALUMINUM THROW-OFF

This spark plug is shorted by aluminum throw-off, which means that particles of the piston are being deposited on the hot insulator of the spark plug.

GAP BRIDGING

Core bridging is caused by using the wrong type of motor oil.

colored. If the porcelain is chalky white or has flaky blisters, the spark plug is too hot. When an engine is operating at high speed with a spark plug that is too hot, it will run along evenly for a while, slow down, pick up speed again, and repeat this balking over and over. If a smutty or oily coating appears on the spark plug, it shows that there is incomplete fuel combustion because the plug is too cold. Hard starting generally is caused by too cold a spark plug.

The spark plug's main job is to transfer the ignition system's energy into the cylinder in the form of a spark. If a normal fuel charge fails to ignite, the spark plug is misfiring. Most misfirings result from shorting through deposits on the insulator nose surface. When these are removed either by cleaning or, in some cases, by burning them off at high speeds, the spark plug's firing ability is restored. This type of shorting is troublesome in that it can occur long before it is noticed. An owner is not always aware of a slow decrease in performance and economy because one or more cylinders are misfiring.

Spark Plug Troubles

Extensive tests have shown that spark plug life is directly related to the gasoline used in the engine. Much of the spark plug trouble is simply lead fouling, resulting from the use of automotive gasolines with tetraethyl lead. There is no practical way of removing this lead from the fuel in the field. Lead fouling may be identified by the presence of small yellow or brown globules on the plug.

Some spark plug trouble is caused by excessive carbon formation in the combustion chamber, with eventual fouling of the plug by the carbon particles. It is natural for all internal combustion engines to form some carbon during operation, but excessive amounts are caused by use of fuels which burn to a gummy residue rather than to a fluffy carbon that can pass out with the exhaust. Cracked gasolines result in fuels which give gummy deposits that remain in the combustion chamber, while straight-run gasolines are cleaner in this respect.

The use of a marine white gasoline virtually will eliminate problems with the spark plug and the carbon or varnish formation. Marine white gasolines are straight-run fuels which contain no tetraethyl lead or other metallic additives and are excellent from the standpoint of engine cleanliness. They generally have an octane rating of 75 to 80 and should not be confused with the nonmarine "whites" sold for use in gasoline lamps

The spark plug insulator should be cleaned of all foreign matter, because this could become a leakage path for the high-tension voltage.

When the dirty insulator of a spark plug gets wet, flash-over occurs, and the cylinder misfires.

and cook stoves. The 90 octane aviation gasolines, as used in light aircraft, are limited to 0.5 cc of lead and are suitable for outboard use.

In cases where spark plug or carbon difficulties are being encountered, it is suggested that a change be made to another fuel. If excessive carbon has already formed in the engine, it should be removed by disassembly or with an engine cleaner.

Many so-called spark plug troubles in reality are not traceable to faulty spark plugs. Instead, they result from poor spark plug installation, abnormal operating conditions, ignition defects, over-rich fuel mixtures, fuel mixtures with too much oil, or engines in need of an overhaul.

Used spark plugs are generally the best guide to the type and source of trouble. Therefore, it is good practice to inspect each spark plug as it is removed from the engine. A gasket which is compressed to about 3/4 of its original thickness, with smooth, parallel surfaces, indicates that the spark plug was properly installed and tightened. Gaskets which are compressed too much or too little reveal improper tightening. Rough and corroded surfaces indicate that the gasket seats were not cleaned before installation. In some cases, the resulting

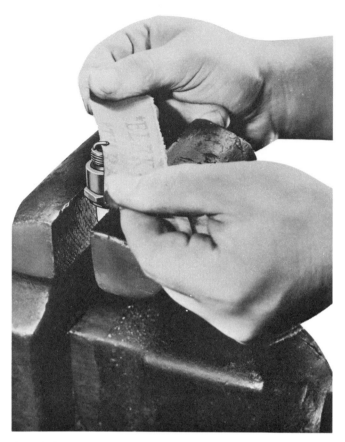

One of the most important spark plug service procedures is to file the electrodes to remove the corrosion. This mechanic is passing a piece of emery cloth between the electrodes to clean the metal.

compression leakage may have overheated the spark plugs to cause excessive electrode erosion. *NOTE: Some spark plugs have conical seats and, therefore, do not use a gasket.*

Spark plugs that are not tightened securely will cause fast electrode burning, and they may burn the piston due to detonation. Torque spark plugs to 20 ft-lbs. for a good seat.

Fuel fouling can be identified by wet, black deposits covering the entire firing end of the spark plug. These deposits result from incomplete combustion, which is traceable to an over-rich air-fuel mixture.

A crack in the insulator is sufficient cause for discarding the spark plug. Cracks in the upper portion of the insulator are caused by dropping the plug or by hitting the insulator with a wrench. For this reason, always use a deep-socket wrench of the proper size when removing or installing the spark plugs, and support the upper end with the palm of your hand to keep it from tilting enough to touch the insulator. Cracked or broken insulator firing ends result from bending the center electrode while setting the spark plug gap. To avoid damaging the insulator, bend only the side electrode.

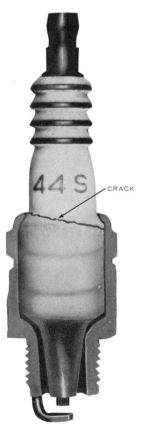

A cracked insulator can be caused only by tilting the spark plug socket.

Always bend the ground electrode to adjust the gap. If you bend the center electrode, you will crack the porcelain.

Other engine conditions can cause spark plug troubles. In general, ignition timing advanced beyond specifications will encourage overheating, thus leading to shorter spark plug life and burned pistons. Burned, pitted, or improperly set breaker points and frayed ignition cables also are sources of spark plug trouble.

It is important to keep the upper portion of the spark plug insulators free from moisture, grease, dirt, and paint. Such deposits on the outside of a spark plug can cause surface shorting or flashover from the terminal to the shell, with resulting misfire and hard starting. Spark plug insulators should be wiped off periodically with a clean rag.

Spark Plug Protectors

When installing a new set of spark plugs, inspect the spark plug protectors carefully for possible damage. No rubber will withstand indefinitely the heat of a spark plug operating under modern conditions, particularly with the high-temperature fuels now being used. When this rubber is stretched tight around the hot porcelain, the effect is to cause the rubber to dry out and crack. Once this has happened, the effectiveness of the spark plug protector as a waterproof seal is seriously impaired.

The sensitive area, where heat and stretch are greatest, is the inside bottom rim where it touches the porcelain. When this edge becomes hard, it loses its strength. The next phase is a series of fine cracks in the surface of the rubber along this same edge. It is safest to replace the spark plug protector when this edge gets hard, before it has a chance to start cracking.

The spark plug protector is not meant to be taken apart. Doing so will usually bend the prong in the spring,

making it all but impossible to reassemble correctly. Don't pull the cable out of the spark plug protector except when the protector and spring are to be replaced.

When assembling a spark plug protector to a cable, make sure that the prong of the spring goes through the center of the cable to make solid contact with the ignition wire. If this is not a good electrical contact, a weak spark may result. Also, the point on this prong should always face down toward the spark plug. If it is assembled upside down, the spark plug protector may have a tendency to shake loose.

MAGNETO SERVICE PROCEDURES

ONE- AND TWO-CYLINDER ENGINES

The magneto consists of breaker points, condensers, and coils. These ignition parts are located under the flywheel; therefore, to service the ignition system of these smaller engines, it is necessary to remove the flywheel.

Distributor service procedures for the larger engines will be covered in the second section of this chapter, under the tuning instructions for the three-cylinder engine.

REMOVING THE FLYWHEEL

Remove the flywheel nut and lockwasher. Install a knock-off tool and turn it down to within two turns of the flywheel. Lift up on the edge of the flywheel, and then strike the knock-off tool with a medium-weight hammer. The blow must be centered as much as possible. *CAUTION: Don't use a heavy hammer or strike the tool too hard; you may damage the crankshaft and bearings.*

BREAKER POINT SERVICE

Generally, it is best to replace the breaker points before tuning an engine because of the load that they carry and the effect that they have on the operating efficiency of the engine. If new breaker points are not available, they can be cleaned in an emergency by folding a small strip of 320-grit emery cloth and inserting it between the points. Hold the points closed and rotate the emery cloth, using the points as a pivot. Open the points to remove the emery cloth. *CAUTION: Don't pull the cloth from between the points, or you will scrape off emery particles, which are an insulator.* Remove all traces of emery by inserting a clean piece of cardboard between the breaker points, and then (holding the points closed on the cardboard) rotate the cardboard, using the

CONTACT POINT

This black, pitted breaker point shows evidence of oil on the contact surface, which burned into an insulator. The oil can be placed on the contact point surface with your fingers or by using a dirty feeler gauge to measure the gap.

breaker points as a pivot, in order to remove the oxide and other foreign matter loosened by the emery cloth. The cardboard should be used in several spots until no further dirt can be removed.

To adjust the breaker point gap, move the throttle to the wide-open position to establish a common stationary location for setting the breaker points. Reinstall the flywheel nut so that you can turn the crankshaft with a box wrench. Rotate the crankshaft clockwise at least two full turns to establish a uniform grease film, and then rotate it enough to bring the breaker point cam follower to the high point of the cam (index line). *CAUTION: If the crankshaft is turned too far, it must be rotated an additional turn clockwise to reach the mark. Never turn the crankshaft in a counterclockwise direction to correct.*

Adjust the breaker point gap to specifications. *CAUTION: Always use a smooth, unworn feeler gauge blade and always make sure that the gaps are identical on two-cylinder engines so that the points will be synchronized. An error of 0.0015" will change the ignition timing as much as 1°. CAUTION: Always clean the feeler gauge blade before inserting it between the points to prevent depositing a layer of oil, which will cause operating difficulties later on.*

Lubricate the breaker cam, breaker plate pilot bore, cam wiper felt, and all friction surfaces of the ignition system with Rykon No. 2EP. Other types of lubricants will cause ignition troubles and operating difficulties.

BREAKER POINT SYNCHRONIZATION

On the larger two-cylinder engines, point synchronization is an important adjustment. Its purpose is to make sure that the spark occurs at precisely the same instant for each cylinder. Generally, the gap of the second set of breaker points is varied from the initial setting to obtain synchronization.

Breaker point cleaning and gapping must always precede synchronization. Changing the gap of either set of points will change both the timing and synchronization. After the breaker points are cleaned and gapped, the first set of breaker points should be timed to the top piston. Then, without moving the stator plate, the timing gauge should be transferred to the bottom cylinder and the gap of the second set of breaker points adjusted so that the spark will occur at the same position of the second piston.

Smaller engines are not sensitive to breaker point synchronization, and the manufacturer generally specifies that it is only necessary to gap the breaker points evenly. If the gaps are even, synchronization is close enough for all practical purposes. For engines on which breaker point synchronization is called for by the manufacturer, this adjustment will be covered in the second section of this chapter, under the tuning instructions for the individual engines.

IGNITION TIMING

The ignition spark must occur at precisely the instant it will do the most good. This means that the spark must occur close to TDC at idle speed and about 30° before TDC at high rpms. This ignition advance is required to compensate for the time lag between the start of combustion and the development of maximum pressure. At high engine speeds, it is necessary to start combustion about 30° BTDC so that maximum combustion chamber pressure will be reached when the piston reaches the top of the stroke.

The method of timing the engine varies, but most of the larger engines have the flywheel marked at the TDC position. In addition, some are marked at the specified Maximum Spark Advance point for setting the timing with the throttle at the wide-open position. These instructions vary with engine types and will be discussed in detail under each of the engine headings.

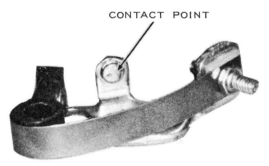

CONTACT POINT

The frosted appearance of this breaker point is an indication that the ignition system was operating properly.

This hole in the piston crown is the result of runaway surface ignition. It can be caused by a lean carburetor mixture or the ignition timing's being too far advanced.

A burned piston is the result of incorrect tuning adjustments or a clogged cooling system. Always make tuning adjustments accurately.

TUNE-UP SPECIFICATIONS

MODEL	SPARK PLUGS TYPE Champion	AC	GAP (Inches)	BREAKER POINT GAP (Inches)	CONDENSER CAPACITY (Mfds)	FULL-THROTTLE RANGE (Rpm)	IDLE SPEED IN GEAR (Rpm)	MAXIMUM SPARK ADVANCE (Degrees before TDC)
3.5	H10J	M46L	.035	.020	.15–.19	3,100–3,900	700–800	—
3.6	H10J	M46L	.035	.020	.15–.19	3,600–4,400	700–800	—
4.0	J14Y	M45S	.035	.020	.16–.18	3,400–4,000	450–550	—
7.5	H10J	M46L	.035	.020	.15–.19	4,200–4,800	800	—
9	—	6S45T	.035	.020	.15–.19	4,800–5,800	800	—
2	J6J	M44B	.035	.020	.15–.19	4,400–5,200	600	—
4	J6J	M44B	.035	.020	.15–.19	4,600–5,400	600	—
25	J6J	M44B	.035	.020	.26–.30	4,400–5,200	500	—
27	J6J	M44B	.035	.020	.26–.30	4,400–5,200	700	—
28	J4J	M42K	.035	.020	.26–.30	4,400–5,200	700	—
0	J6J	M44B	.035	.020	.26–.30	4,400–5,200	700	33
3 Manual	J4J	M42K	.035	.020	.26–.30	4,600–5,400	700	31
3 Elect.	UJ17V	—	—	.020	.26–.30	4,600–5,400	700	31
5 Manual	J4J	M42K	.035	.020	.26–.30	4,800–5,600	700–800	31
5 Elect.	UJ17V	—	—	.020n	.26–.30	4,800–5,600	700–800	31
0	J6J	—	.035	.020n	.25–.27	4,400–5,200	600	28
5	UJ17V	—	—	.020n	.25–.27	4,800–5,600	800–950	28 ①

① In 1962, set the Maximum Spark Advance to 25°. In 1963, set it to 25° (1st phase) and to 28° (3rd phase).

CARBURETOR THROTTLE PICKUP ADJUSTMENT

The throttle control of all small outboard motors is connected to the magneto stator plate. Opening the throttle advances the stator plate (and the ignition timing). The stator plate is linked to the carburetor throttle, so that opening the throttle and advancing the stator plate opens the carburetor throttle valves at the same time. One of the most important tuning procedures is the throttle pick-up adjustment; the point of spark advance at which the throttle valves begin to open. This adjustment, called the Carburetor-Timing Synchronous Adjustment, will be covered in the second section of this chapter, under the tuning instructions for the individual engines.

ONE-CYLINDER TUNE-UP PROCEDURES

3.5 & 4 Hp Engines

① A flywheel-type magneto furnishes the spark for these engines. Moving the speed-control lever shifts the entire stator plate, which affects the ignition timing. A throttle-actuating cam, attached to the speed-control lever, synchronizes throttle valve opening to ignition timing.

BREAKER POINT SERVICE

② Install new breaker points, and then gap them to 0.020″ with the breaker arm on the high point of the cam. No synchronous adjustment is required.

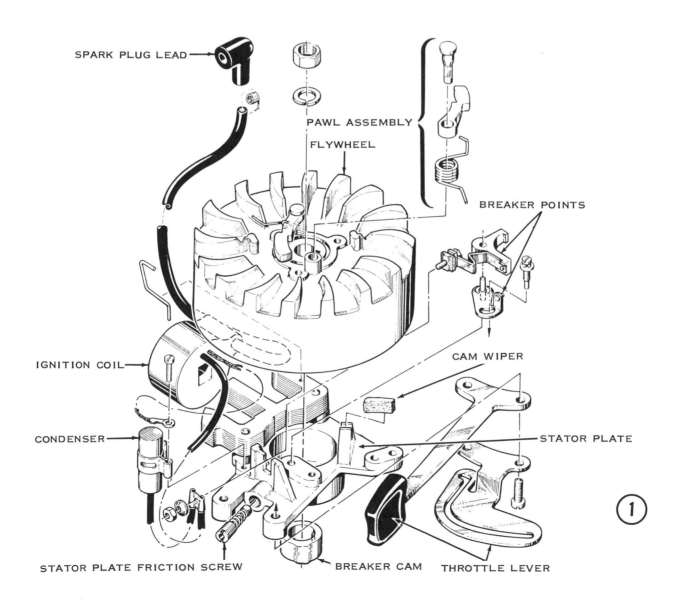

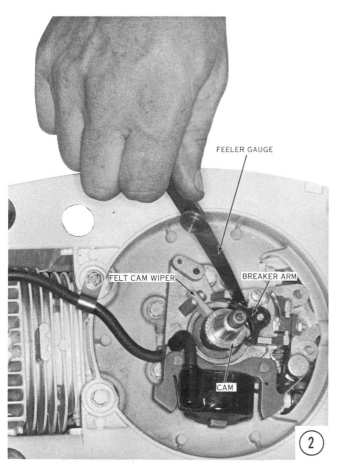

CARBURETOR ADJUSTMENTS

③ Warm the engine to operating temperature. Turn the idle mixture adjusting screw until the engine idles steadily. The engine must not stop when the speed-control lever is returned to the idle position.

④ Turn the high-speed adjusting screw for maximum speed, spanning the range between rich and lean. Set the adjustment at the mid-point of the range, preferably closer to the rich side. Accelerate the engine. If it hesitates, open the idle mixture adjusting screw 1/8 turn at a time until the acceleration is smooth.

TWO-CYLINDER ENGINE TUNE-UP SERVICE PROCEDURES

7.5, 9 & 12/14 Hp Engines

⑤ A flywheel-type magneto furnishes the spark for these engines. Turning the twist-grip handle shifts the entire stator plate, which affects the ignition timing. A throttle-actuating cam, attached to the stator plate, synchronizes throttle valve opening with ignition timing.

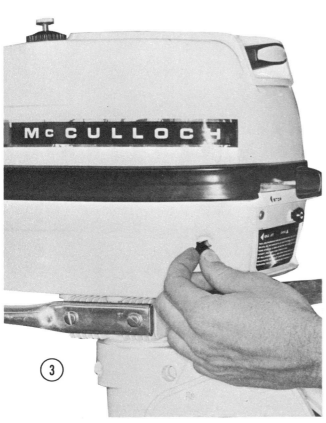

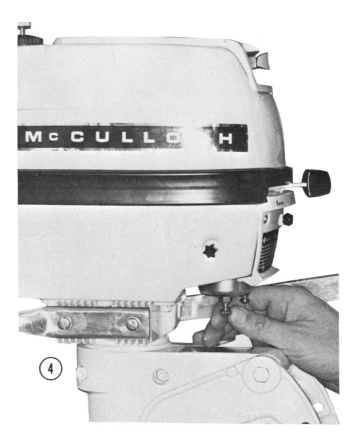

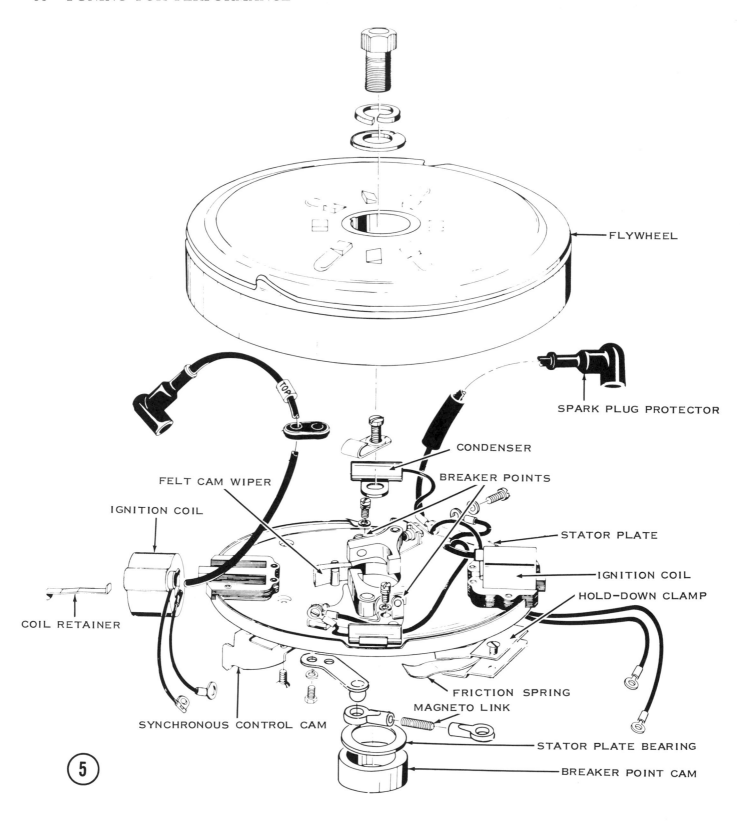

FLYWHEEL

SPARK PLUG PROTECTOR

CONDENSER

FELT CAM WIPER

BREAKER POINTS

IGNITION COIL

STATOR PLATE

IGNITION COIL

HOLD-DOWN CLAMP

COIL RETAINER

FRICTION SPRING

SYNCHRONOUS CONTROL CAM

MAGNETO LINK

STATOR PLATE BEARING

BREAKER POINT CAM

⑤

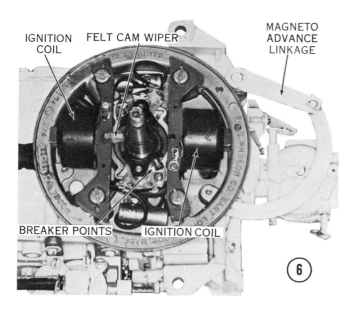

⑥

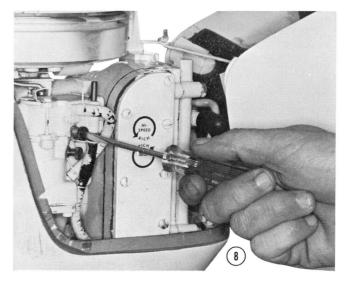

⑧

BREAKER POINT SERVICE

⑥ Install new breaker points, and then gap them to 0.020″ with the breaker arm on the high point of the cam. The two sets of breaker points do not have to be synchronized, provided that they are gapped to exactly 0.020″.

CARBURETOR-TIMING SYNCHRONOUS ADJUSTMENT

⑦ Throttle valve opening must be synchronized with magneto timing. Check this adjustment by turning the twist-grip handle to the SLOW position, and then slowly turning it to the FAST position. The synchronous control arm must contact the synchronous cam at the index mark. If necessary, turn the adjusting screw until the control arm just makes contact with the cam at the index mark. Retard the throttle and recheck the adjustment.

CARBURETOR ADJUSTMENTS

⑧ Warm the engine to operating temperature. Shift into FORWARD gear and set the twist-grip handle to the FAST position. Turn the high-speed adjusting screw

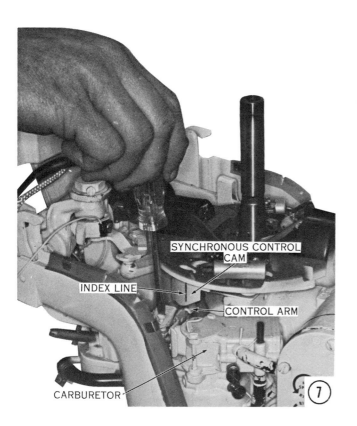

⑦

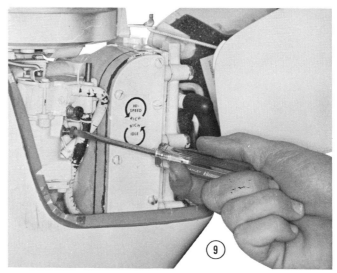

⑨

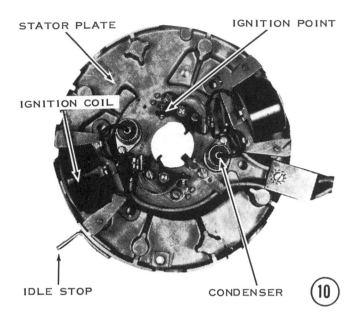

STATOR PLATE · IGNITION POINT
IGNITION COIL
IDLE STOP · CONDENSER ⑩

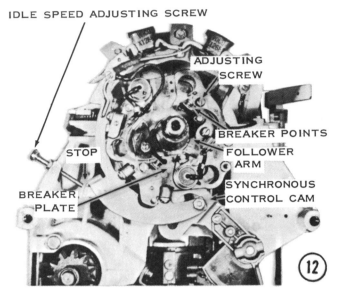

IDLE SPEED ADJUSTING SCREW
ADJUSTING SCREW
STOP · BREAKER POINTS · FOLLOWER ARM · SYNCHRONOUS CONTROL CAM
BREAKER PLATE ⑫

in and out to span the range from rich to lean, and then set the adjusting screw near the mid-point, preferably closer to the rich side.

⑨ With the engine in FORWARD gear, turn the idle speed adjusting screw to a position where the engine runs smoothly. Turn the idle mixture adjusting screw in

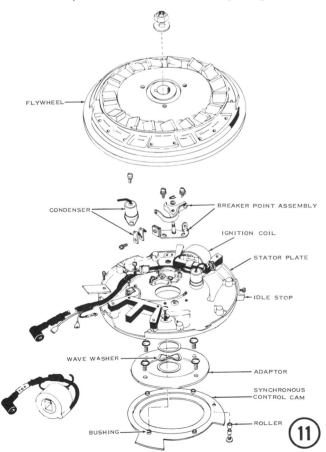

FLYWHEEL
CONDENSER · BREAKER POINT ASSEMBLY
IGNITION COIL
STATOR PLATE
IDLE STOP
WAVE WASHER · ADAPTOR
SYNCHRONOUS CONTROL CAM
BUSHING · ROLLER ⑪

and out, spanning the range between rich and lean, and then set the mixture adjusting screw at the mid-point of the range. Readjust the idle speed adjusting screw to obtain the lowest idle speed consistent with smooth operation. Accelerate the engine. If it hesitates, open the high-speed adjusting screw 1/8 turn at a time until the engine accelerates smoothly. Recheck the idle mixture adjusting screw to obtain a smooth idle.

TWO-CYLINDER ENGINE TUNE-UP SERVICE PROCEDURES

25/28 Hp Engines

⑩ Two types of ignition systems are used on these models: a flywheel-type magneto with a rope-type starter and a battery-ignition system with an electric cranking motor. The only difference is that the magneto-type ignition coils are mounted on the stator plate, inside of the flywheel as shown in this illustration. The engine with a battery-ignition system has two ignition coils mounted on the cylinder head. This latter ignition system requires an external ballast resistor, which is mounted on the dash panel.

BREAKER POINT SERVICE

⑪ Install new breaker points, and then gap them to 0.020″ with the breaker arm on the high point of the cam. The two sets of breaker points do not have to be synchronized, provided that they are gapped to exactly 0.020″.

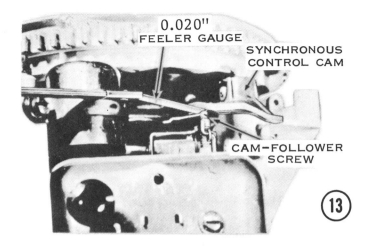

0.020"
FEELER GAUGE
SYNCHRONOUS CONTROL CAM
CAM-FOLLOWER SCREW

⑬

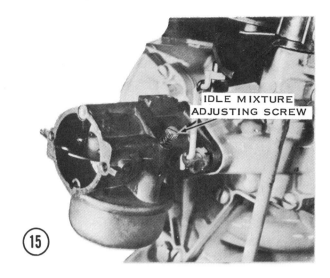

IDLE MIXTURE ADJUSTING SCREW

⑮

CARBURETOR-TIMING SYNCHRONOUS ADJUSTMENT

Neutral Speed Limit Adjustment

⑫ The neutral speed limit adjustment prevents engine overspeed while in NEUTRAL gear. To make this adjustment, shift into NEUTRAL and retard the throttle lever. Bring the synchronous control cam idle stop against the idle speed adjusting screw. Turn the idle

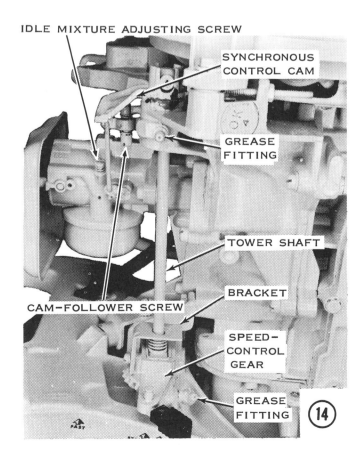

IDLE MIXTURE ADJUSTING SCREW
SYNCHRONOUS CONTROL CAM
GREASE FITTING
TOWER SHAFT
CAM-FOLLOWER SCREW
BRACKET
SPEED-CONTROL GEAR
GREASE FITTING

⑭

speed adjusting screw until 1/4" space exists between the limiter beam and the synchronous cam fast-idle stop.

⑬ Make a preliminary fast-idle speed adjustment by turning the cam-follower screw so that it is 0.020" below the cam surface.

CARBURETOR ADJUSTMENTS

⑭ To make the fast-idle speed adjustment, advance the throttle to the fast-idle stop, shift into NEUTRAL, start the engine, and warm it to operating temperature. Adjust the cam-follower screw so that the engine idles at 1,800–2,000 rpm.

⑮ Turn the idle mixture adjusting screw until the engine idles smoothly, and then accelerate it quickly. If the engine backfires, open the adjusting screw 1/8 turn at a time until the engine accelerates smoothly. After completing the adjustments, run the engine at wide-open throttle for at least 30 seconds, and then decelerate quickly. If the engine stops, open the idle mixture adjusting screw another 1/8 turn.

TWO-CYLINDER ENGINE TUNE-UP SERVICE PROCEDURES

40–45 Hp Engines

These engines come equipped with either a battery-ignition system and an electric cranking motor or a flywheel-type magneto and a recoil-type starter. The ignition breaker points are located under the flywheel and two ignition coils are mounted on the powerhead for both models. A ballast resistor is secured to the dash panel on models with a battery-ignition system.

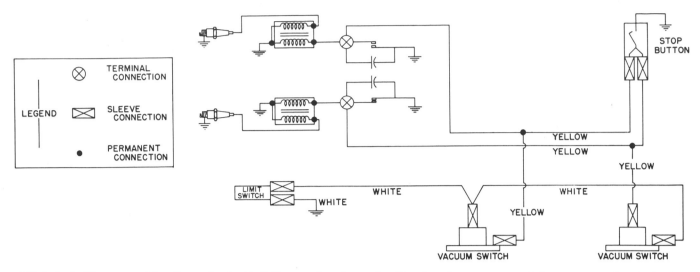

This is the ignition system wiring diagram for the 40–45 Hp manual-starting engine. Note how the two vacuum switches are connected to the breaker points. Their function is to ground out the breaker points through the limit switch if the throttle is retarded but engine speed does not decrease.

The electric-starting engine has a shift-limit switch and a neutral overspeed limit lock. The shift-limit switch is wired in series with the cranking motor solenoid to prevent the engine from starting while in gear. The neutral overspeed limit lock prevents the throttle from being advanced too far when the engine is in NEUTRAL.

The manual-starting models (and electric-starting models in some years) have a special safety circuit switch incorporated to prevent excessively high rpm in the event that the engine does not respond to normal throttle control. The circuit includes two vacuum switches (operated by crankcase vacuum) and a throttle switch, which is operated by a cam on the tower shaft. The circuit is wired so that the throttle switch and one of the vacuum switches is connected in series with each set of ignition breaker points. One side of the throttle switch is connected to ground.

With the throttle control lever at the idle position, the throttle switch circuit is closed, completing that part of the circuit to ground. In the event that the engine does not respond to normal throttle control, the increase in manifold vacuum will close the vacuum switches, grounding out the breaker points and stopping the engine. The throttle switch must be adjusted to ensure the safety feature of this circuit.

VACUUM AND THROTTLE SWITCH ADJUSTMENTS

The vacuum switch cannot be adjusted but, if the circuit is not functioning properly, it is necessary to remove the switch housing to check the condition of the diaphragm.

To adjust the throttle switch, attach the small test leads from a self-powered timing lamp to the throttle switch terminals, shift into NEUTRAL, and then advance the throttle to the fast-idle position so that the limiter plate bottoms against the stop lever. Loosen the throttle shaft cam and rotate it until the test lamp lights, indicating that the switch contacts are closed. Tighten the throttle cam and recheck the adjustment.

This is the ignition system wiring diagram for the electric starting 40–45 Hp engine. Note the single vacuum switch that is connected to the breaker points. Its function is to ground out the breaker points through the limit switch if the throttle is retarded but engine speed does not decrease.

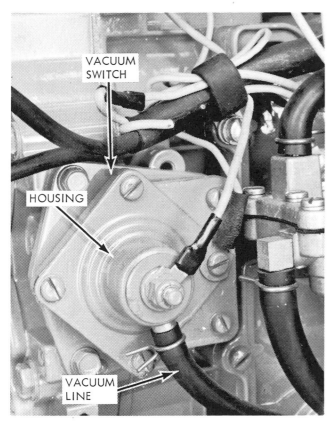

The vacuum switch cannot be adjusted, but it should be removed to check the condition of the diaphragm if the circuit is not functioning normally.

SHIFT-LIMIT SWITCH

Electric Starting Models

This shift-limit switch keeps the starting motor from operating when the shift lever is in gear.

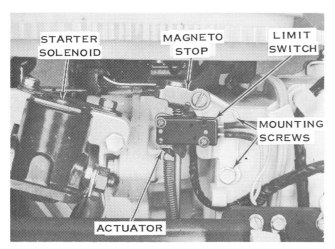

The shift-limit switch prevents the starting motor from operating when the shift lever is in gear. It must be adjusted as discussed in the text.

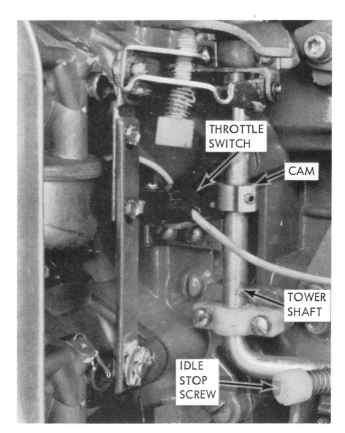

The throttle switch must be adjusted as discussed in the text.

Models through 1962

Adjust the switch by loosening the switch mounting bracket screws. With the shift lever in NEUTRAL, position the switch so that the plunger is fully depressed, and then lock the mounting screws.

Models since 1963

The shift-limit switch must be adjusted by moving the throttle lever to the slow-idle position and then shifting into NEUTRAL. Adjust the nut at the top of the lock rod so that the limit plate bottoms against the magneto stop when the throttle is advanced. When the shift lever is in FORWARD or REVERSE gear, the limit arm must not bottom.

IGNITION SERVICE PROCEDURES

① Two sets of breaker points are located under the flywheel, and they must be spaced and then synchronized with each other. Replace the breaker points, and then gap them to 0.020″ for a preliminary adjustment. Timing and point synchronization is accomplished by checking the opening of each point set against flywheel markings. The gaps of the breaker points may have to be varied for both timing and synchronization.

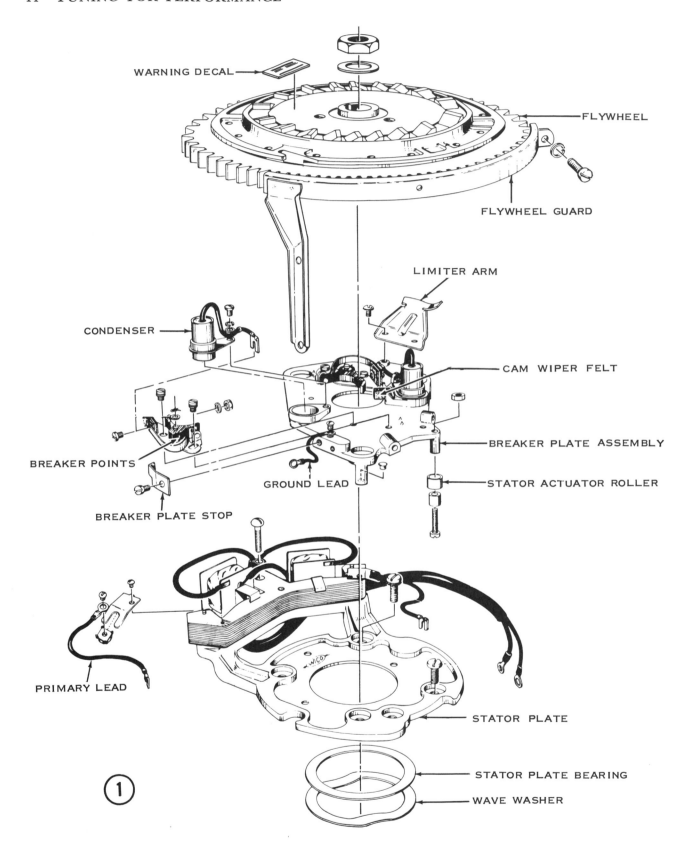

WARNING DECAL →

FLYWHEEL

FLYWHEEL GUARD

LIMITER ARM

CONDENSER →

CAM WIPER FELT

BREAKER PLATE ASSEMBLY

BREAKER POINTS

GROUND LEAD

STATOR ACTUATOR ROLLER

BREAKER PLATE STOP

PRIMARY LEAD

STATOR PLATE

STATOR PLATE BEARING

WAVE WASHER

①

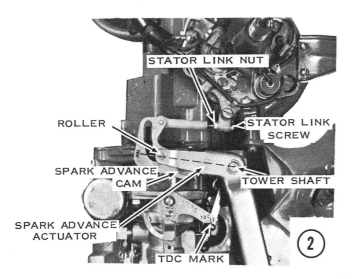

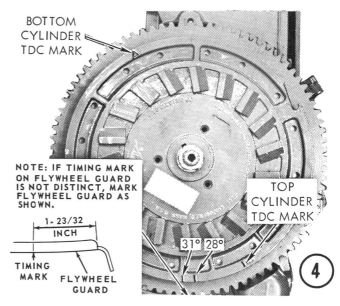

MAXIMUM SPARK ADVANCEMENT ADJUSTMENT

40/43 Hp Engines with Carter Carburetors and Adjustable Linkage

② These engines are timed to TDC rather than to a Maximum Spark Advance position. To make the adjustment, shift into NEUTRAL and move the speed control lever as far toward the FAST position as possible. *NOTE: This places the stator against the stator stop.* Loosen the nut on the stator link screw, and then turn the stator screw in or out until the TDC mark on the spark advance cam, the center of the roller on the spark advance actuator, and the center of the tower shaft are aligned, as shown. Tighten the locknut.

MAXIMUM SPARK ADVANCE ADJUSTMENT

43 Hp Engines (Royal Scott Electric Models) with Carter Carburetors

③ Place the shift lever in FORWARD gear, and

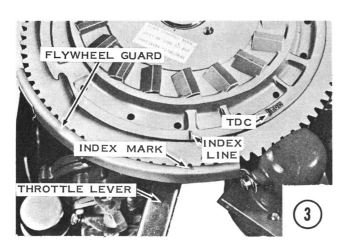

then advance the throttle lever to the FAST position. Loosen the locknut on the stator link screw, and then adjust the screw until the stop on the limiter arm just comes into contact with the stator plate. Tighten the locknut. Connect a self-powered timing lamp to the breaker points and ground, and then rotate the flywheel in a clockwise direction until the 31° mark is aligned with the index line on the flywheel guard. The breaker points must just open. If necessary, turn the stator link screw in or out to obtain the correct position. The timing of the bottom cylinder can be determined by placing a mark on the flywheel, 180° from the top-cylinder mark (31°). Turn the flywheel clockwise 1/2 turn and the bottom cylinder breaker points should just open as the lines index. If necessary, adjust the breaker point gap of the second set of points until the timing is correct.

MAXIMUM SPARK ADVANCE ADJUSTMENT

43/45 Hp Engines with Marvel-Schebler or Walbro Carburetors and Fixed Linkage

④ The ignition timing is adjusted to the Maximum Spark Advance position with the throttle wide open. The flywheel is marked with an index line (and the letters TDC) for the top cylinder and a raised triangle for the TDC position of the bottom cylinder. It is necessary to locate the Maximum Spark Advance position on the flywheel for each cylinder with a template.

⑤ To make the Maximum Spark Advance timing adjustment for the top cylinder, advance the tower shaft to the wide-open throttle position. Connect a self-powered timing lamp to the primary terminal of the top ignition

MOUNT THIS PAGE ON A STIFF PIECE OF MATERIAL AND CUT ALONG EDGE OF TEMPLATE AND REMOVE.

ALIGN WITH EDGE OF FLYWHEEL

ALIGN WITH EDGE OF FLYWHEEL

33 32 30 29 27 26

31°

28°

ALIGN THIS MARK WITH TDC MARK ON FLYWHEEL

TDC

This template can be used on the flywheel to locate the Maximum Spark Advance position. To use it, paste the template on a piece of stiff cardboard and cut along the curved and back edges. Position the template against the flywheel with the TDC template mark aligned with the TDC mark on the flywheel. Use a pencil to mark the flywheel at the specified Maximum Spark Advance position, according to the engine being timed.

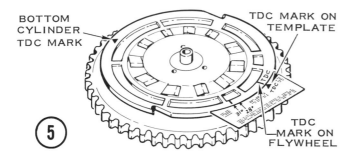

BOTTOM CYLINDER TDC MARK

TDC MARK ON TEMPLATE

⑤

TDC MARK ON FLYWHEEL

coil and ground. Turn the flywheel in a clockwise direction until the first set of breaker points just open. The specified timing mark on the flywheel must be aligned with the index line on the flywheel guard. *CAUTION: There are two marks on the guard on some models. For ignition timing, always use the one which is in line with the center of the engine.* If the first set of breaker points open too early, adjust the point gap slightly closer, and then repeat the test. To advance the timing, widen the breaker point gap. To check the timing (and point synchronization) of the second set of breaker points (bottom cylinder), connect the timing lamp test clip to the primary terminal of the bottom ignition coil and repeat the test. Adjust the breaker point gap for the second set of points for timing (and point synchronization).

CARBURETOR-TIMING SYNCHRONOUS ADJUSTMENT

40/43 Hp Engines with Carter Carburetors and Adjustable Linkage

⑥ The linkage between the tower shaft and the carburetor must be synchronized so that throttle opening and ignition timing are varied in unison. After the engine has been timed properly, as discussed in the paragraph on Maximum Spark Advance Adjustment, shift into NEUTRAL. Advance the throttle until the limiter arm hits the stop lever. Loosen the angle- and length-adjustment screws on the throttle actuator arm. Position the TDC mark on the spark advance cam, the center of the roller on the spark advance actuator, and the center of the throttle tower shaft in a line, as shown. Move the

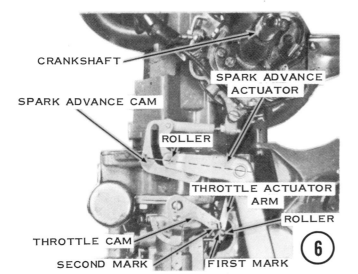

CRANKSHAFT

SPARK ADVANCE ACTUATOR

SPARK ADVANCE CAM

ROLLER

THROTTLE ACTUATOR ARM

ROLLER

THROTTLE CAM

SECOND MARK

FIRST MARK

⑥

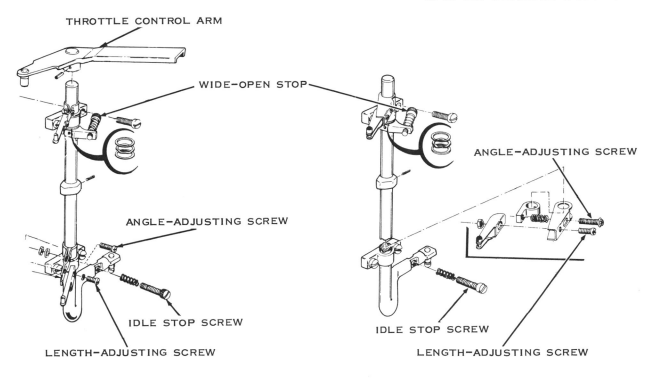

FIRST VERSION   SECOND VERSION

These are the length- and angle-adjustment screws referred to in the text. The tower shaft illustrated at the left is the early version and the one at the right the second type.

throttle actuator arm toward the throttle cam, using both the angle- and the length-adjustment screws until the roller is even with the first mark on the cam, as shown. Tighten the length-adjustment screw.

⑦ Turn the angle-adjustment screw until the center of the roller is even with the second index line, as shown. Repeat this operation with the other carburetor. This procedure just cracks the throttle valves slightly for easy starting and smooth acceleration.

CARBURETOR-TIMING SYNCHRONOUS ADJUSTMENT

43 Hp Engines with Carter Carburetors and Adjustable Linkage

⑧ The adjustments are made in exactly the same way as in the earlier models, except that the linkage has been redesigned so that the length- and angle-adjustment screws are now located on the shaft, as shown.

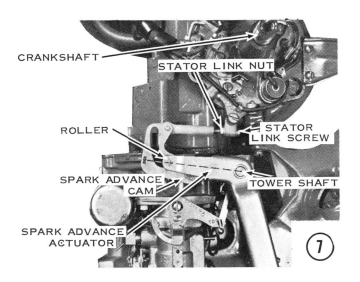

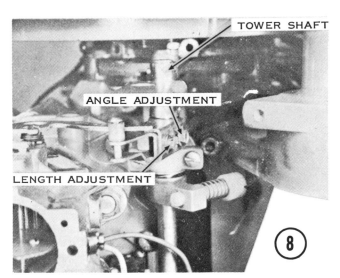

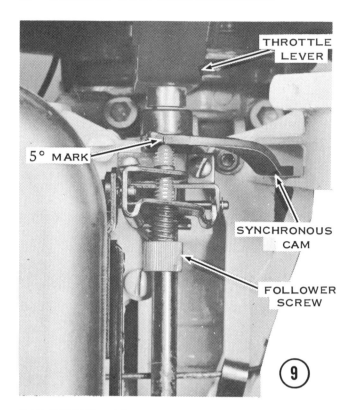

CARBURETOR-TIMING
SYNCHRONOUS ADJUSTMENT

45 Hp Engines with Walbro Carburetors

⑨ The linkage between the tower shaft and the carburetor must be synchronized so that throttle opening and ignition timing are varied in unison. After the engine has been timed properly, as discussed in the paragraph on Maximum Spark Advance Adjustment, advance the throttle lever until the 5° mark on the synchronous control cam is aligned with the cam-follower screw. Turn the screw in until it just contacts the throttle cam at the 5° mark.

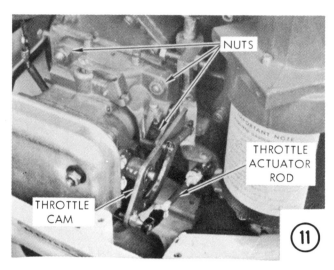

CARBURETOR-TIMING
SYNCHRONOUS ADJUSTMENT

45 Hp Engines with a Marvel-Schebler Carburetor

⑩ The linkage between the tower shaft and the carburetor must be synchronized so that throttle opening and ignition timing are varied in unison. After the engine has been timed properly, as discussed in the paragraph on Maximum Spark Advance Adjustment, turn the flywheel clockwise until the TDC mark for the top cylinder is aligned with the index mark on the flywheel guard. Now, turn the tower shaft slowly until the breaker points just open, as indicated by a self-powered timing lamp's going out.

⑪ Remove the throttle actuator rod between the tower shaft and the carburetor throttle cam. *CAUTION: The tower shaft must not be moved after it has been located properly at the TDC position.*

⑫ Back out the idle speed adjusting screw until the throttle valves are completely closed.

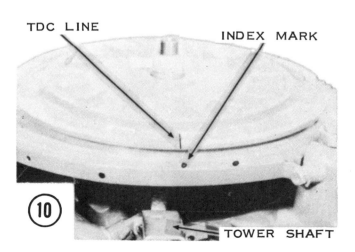

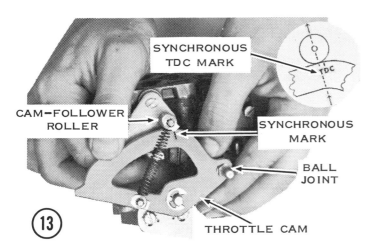

⑬ Hold the carburetor throttle cam so that the stem of the "T" bisects the cam roller. *CAUTION: Disregard the raised mark over the "D."* Now, with the tower shaft at the TDC position and the throttle cam "T" bisecting the cam roller, adjust the length of the throttle actuator rod until it can be slipped onto the ball socket of the cam without changing the alignment.

⑭ With the tower shaft in the fully retarded posi-

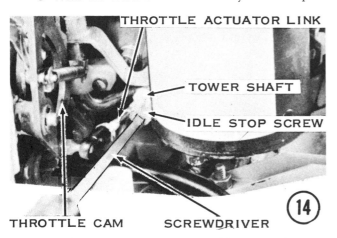

tion, turn the tower shaft idle stop screw out until it does not contact the crankcase, and then turn it in until it just makes contact. Now, turn the tower shaft idle stop screw in two (2) full turns.

⑮ The carburetor idle speed adjusting screw has been backed out fully in Step ⑫. Now, turn it in until it just contacts the throttle arm, and then turn it in one (1) additional turn to establish a preliminary idle speed.

⑯ After the engine is running, it is necessary to make a fast-idle speed adjustment which will open the throttles partially to help in starting a cold engine. With

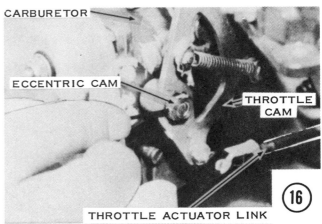

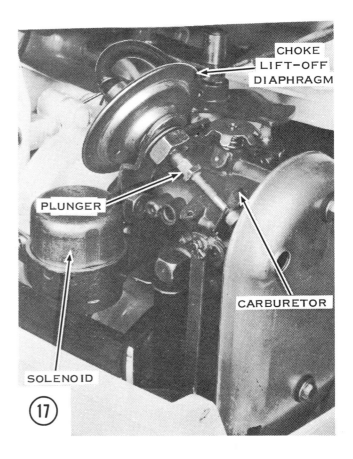

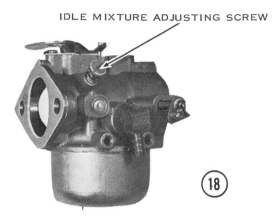

IDLE MIXTURE ADJUSTING SCREW

(18)

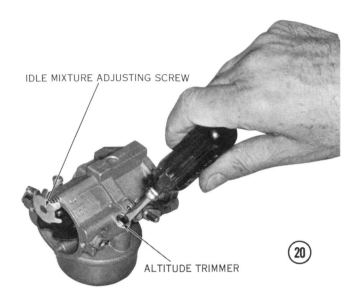

IDLE MIXTURE ADJUSTING SCREW

ALTITUDE TRIMMER

(20)

the engine running in NEUTRAL and with the tower shaft at the fast-idle position, loosen the Allen-headed setscrew on the eccentric cam. Rotate the cam so that the engine idles at 1,400–1,600 rpm. Tighten the setscrew.

VACUUM LIFT-OFF CHOKE

Models with Walbro Carburetors

⑰ The purpose of the vacuum lift-off choke assembly is to keep the operator from overchoking the

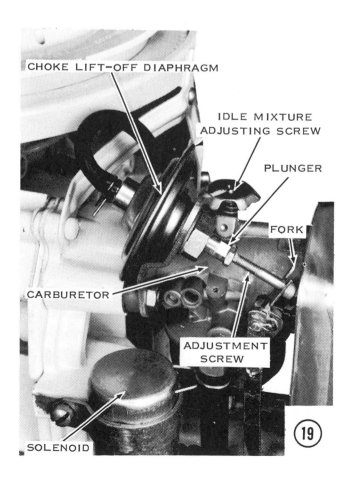

CHOKE LIFT-OFF DIAPHRAGM

IDLE MIXTURE
ADJUSTING SCREW

PLUNGER

FORK

CARBURETOR

ADJUSTMENT
SCREW

SOLENOID

(19)

engine during the starting procedure. To make an adjustment, lift the choke bar to close the choke valves, and then adjust the plunger screw until the underside of the bolt head just comes into contact with the fork on the carburetor shaft. Holding the plunger, tighten the nut against the plunger.

CARBURETOR ADJUSTMENTS

Models with Two Carter Carburetors

⑱ Turn the idle mixture adjusting screw out 3 turns from the fully closed position for a preliminary adjustment. Start the engine and warm it to operating temperature. To make the idle mixture adjustment, shift into FORWARD gear and retard the throttle to the idle position. Turn the idle mixture adjusting screw of the top carburetor clockwise (lean) until the engine pops, and then turn the screw counterclockwise 1/2 turn until the engine just begins to speed up. Repeat this procedure for each carburetor until a smooth idle is obtained.

High-Speed Adjustment

A special high-altitude metering rod is available for engines operating above elevations of 4,000′. *CAUTION: Don't use these special metering rods below 4,000′ because the mixture will be too lean and will cause preignition.*

Models with Two Walbro Carburetors
without High-Speed Trimmers

⑲ Run the engine in FORWARD gear until it reaches operating temperature. Adjust the nylon stop screw on the tower shaft to obtain an idle speed of 900 rpm. *Slowly* turn the idle mixture adjusting screw of the top carburetor in (lean) until the engine pops, and then

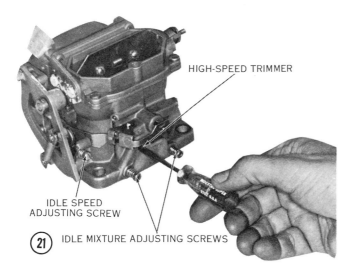

HIGH-SPEED TRIMMER

IDLE SPEED
ADJUSTING SCREW

(21) IDLE MIXTURE ADJUSTING SCREWS

back it out 3/8–1/2 turn. Repeat the adjustment at the bottom carburetor.

Models with Two Walbro Carburetors with High-Speed Trimmers

⓴ Warm the engine for approximately three minutes. Shift into FORWARD gear, and then turn the idle speed adjusting screw to obtain an idle speed of 800–1,000 rpm. Turn the idle mixture adjusting screw of the top carburetor clockwise (lean) until the engine pops, and then back out the screw 1/4 turn. Repeat the adjustment on the other carburetor. If necessary, readjust the idle speed to 800–1,000 rpm.

Altitude Trimmer

This adjustment should be made only at altitudes above 5,000'. To make the adjustment, pry out the seal over each carburetor trimmer. Hook up a tachometer and start the engine. Shift into FORWARD gear and advance the throttle to the wide-open position. Turn the trimmer adjustment clockwise (rich) until the engine speed drops, and then back it out until the speed just begins to increase and the engine runs smoothly. Repeat the adjustment at the other carburetor. *CAUTION: Operating the engine on a lean mixture will cause it to overheat, which will cause severe damage to the powerhead.*

Models with a Marvel-Schebler Carburetor

㉑ With the engine idling and at operating temperature, shift into FORWARD gear, and then move the throttle lever to the idle position. Turn the idle speed adjusting screw until the engine idles at 700–800 rpm.

Slowly turn the port side idle mixture adjusting screw clockwise (lean) until the engine pops, and then back out the screw 1/4 turn. Repeat the adjustment for the starboard side.

High-Speed Trimmer

The high-speed trimmer should be adjusted for maximum speed. Because the trimmer controls only about 10% of the high-speed circuit fuel, the adjustment is not sensitive. On some engines, you may not be able to note any change in speed.

THREE-CYLINDER ENGINE TUNE-UP SERVICE PROCEDURES

75 Hp Engine

This engine is equipped with a battery-ignition system. A belt-driven distributor, with a six-lobe cam, is driven at half crankshaft speed. A single ignition coil is mounted on the powerhead; it furnishes the high-tension voltage to fire the surface-gap type spark plugs. A ballast resistor is mounted on the dash panel.

SHIFT-LIMIT SWITCH

① The function of this switch is to keep the engine from being started while in REVERSE or FORWARD gear. The shift-limit switch should be adjusted by shifting into NEUTRAL. Loosen the screws which hold the mounting bracket, adjust the position of the switch until its nylon plunger is depressed to within 0.015″ of the case, and then tighten the mounting screws. *CAUTION: The engine must be in NEUTRAL for this adjustment.* In FORWARD or REVERSE gear, there must be a minimum of 0.010″ clearance between the switch plunger and the switch actuator.

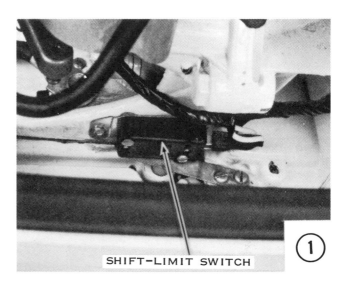

SHIFT-LIMIT SWITCH   ①

FLYWHEEL

TDC MARK

DRIVE BELT

DISTRIBUTOR

②

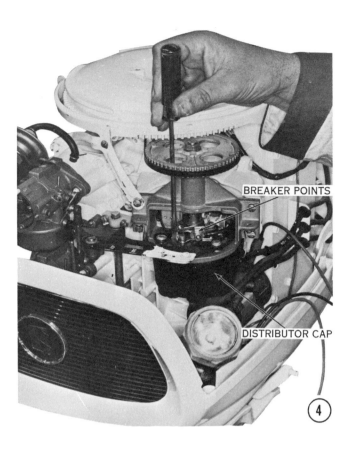

BREAKER POINTS

DISTRIBUTOR CAP

④

DISTRIBUTOR SERVICE

② To install the distributor drive belt, rotate the flywheel until the mark on the distributor pulley, the center of the distributor shaft, the TDC mark on the flywheel, and the center of the crankshaft are in line, and

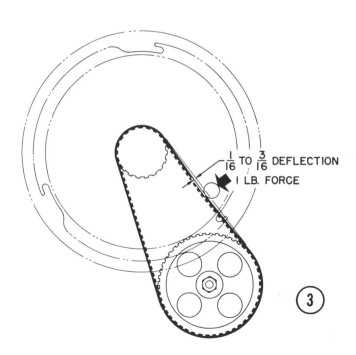

$\frac{1}{16}$ TO $\frac{3}{16}$ DEFLECTION
1 LB. FORCE

③

then slip the drive belt over the distributor pulley. *CAUTION: Be careful not to disturb the position of the flywheel or the distributor pulley.*

③ Tension the drive belt so that it takes a force of one pound to deflect it 1/16″–3/16″ midway between the pulleys. To make this adjustment, place shims of equal thickness between the distributor body and the powerhead mounts until the belt is tensioned correctly. Shims are available in various thicknesses for service.

④ Install new breaker points and adjust the gap to specifications, with the cam follower on the high point of one of the cams. *CAUTION: The correct setting is very important to index the rotor tip properly with the high-tension post in the distributor cap.*

⑤ Adjustment of the spark advance cam places the breaker plate (and breaker points) in the proper relationship with the breaker cam. Rotate the flywheel in a clockwise direction until the TDC mark is aligned with the pointer on the flywheel guard. Connect a timing lamp to the breaker points to determine the exact moment of opening, and then move the spark advance cam so that its TDC mark bisects the center of the spark advance roller, as shown. *NOTE: This adjustment should not be necessary unless someone has tampered with it.* The screw heads and the cam have been painted white on later models so that an unauthorized adjustment can be detected easily. If necessary, move the breaker plate

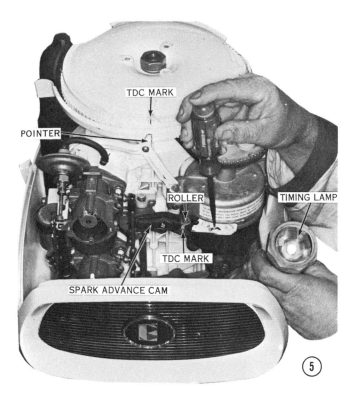

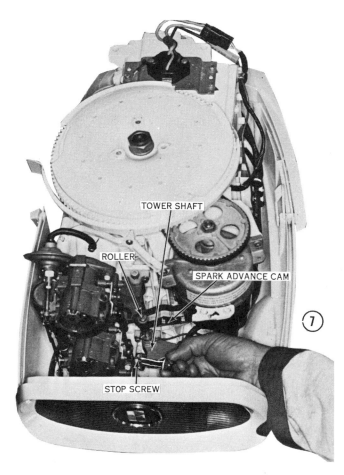

until the breaker points just open, as indicated by the timing lamp's going out.

⑥ In order to check the timing at the wide-open throttle position, rotate the flywheel until the specified Advanced Timing Mark on the flywheel lines up with the

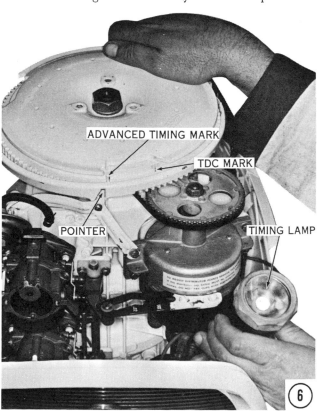

pointer. Now, move the throttle to the wide-open position; the breaker points should open at this point, as indicated by the timing lamp's going out.

⑦ With the throttle in the wide-open position, it is very important that the throttle roller does not contact the end of the spark advance cam; otherwise, the distributor cam can be hammered out of adjustment by the throttle roller. An adjustment should be made to the stop screw at the bottom of the tower shaft so that there is approximately 1/16″ clearance between the spark advance cam and the tower shaft roller.

CARBURETOR-TIMING SYNCHRONOUS ADJUSTMENT

⑧ On all 60 Hp (and 1961 75 Hp) engines, position the spark advance cam so that its TDC mark bisects the center line of the spark advance roller. Holding the spark advance cam and the spark advance roller in this position, move the top throttle actuator arm toward the throttle cam, using both the angle- and the length-adjustment screws until the roller on the actuator arm touches the throttle cam at the TDC mark. Tighten both adjustment screws securely. Repeat this procedure with the remaining actuator arms. Tighten the angle- and the

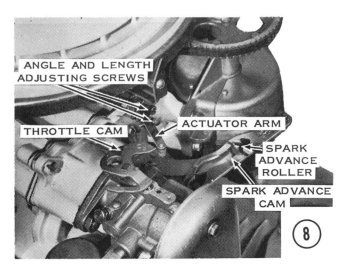

ANGLE AND LENGTH
ADJUSTING SCREWS

THROTTLE CAM

ACTUATOR ARM

SPARK
ADVANCE
ROLLER

SPARK ADVANCE
CAM

(8)

ROLLER

(10)

length-adjustment screws when each actuator arm is positioned correctly. When all three actuator arms have been correctly adjusted, advance the throttle lever slowly and all three actuator arm rollers should contact (and just begin to move) the throttle cams at the same time as the throttle actuator roller leaves the TDC position on the spark advance cam.

⑨ On the 75 Hp engines (from 1962–66), set the TDC mark on the advance cam so that it is bisecting the tower shaft roller, and then turn the nylon cam-follower screw so that it just contacts the synchronous cam. On

1963 engines, this screw should be turned in an additional 1/8 turn.

⑩ On all models since 1967, a roller on a pivot bracket is connected to the throttle valve linkage. The roller should be adjusted by turning the ball joint shell on the rod in or out until the roller just comes into contact with the throttle cam when the TDC mark on the advance cam bisects the tower shaft roller.

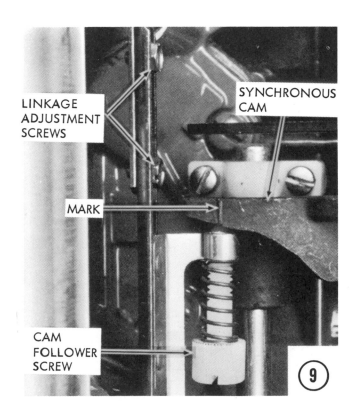

LINKAGE
ADJUSTMENT
SCREWS

SYNCHRONOUS
CAM

MARK

CAM
FOLLOWER
SCREW

(9)

TOWER SHAFT

MAXIMUM ADVANCE
STOP SCREW

IDLE STOP
SCREW

(11)

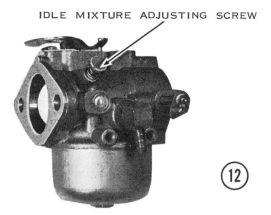

IDLE MIXTURE ADJUSTING SCREW

⑫

CARBURETOR ADJUSTMENTS

Models with Carter Carburetors

⑪ Warm the engine to operating temperature, and then shift into FORWARD gear. Adjust the nylon idle stop screw for a speed of 700–800 rpm.

⑫ Turn the idle mixture adjusting screw on the top carburetor in (lean) until the engine pops, and then back the screw out 3/8–1/2 turn. Repeat the adjustment for the other carburetors.

Models with Walbro Carburetors

⑬ Warm the engine for approximately three minutes. Shift into FORWARD gear, and then turn the idle stop screw to obtain an idle speed of 800–1,000 rpm. Turn the idle mixture adjusting screw on the top carburetor clockwise (lean) until the engine pops, and then back out the screw 1/4 turn. Repeat the adjustment on the other carburetors. If necessary, readjust the idle speed to 800–1,000 rpm.

Altitude Trimmer

Models since 1964

This adjustment should be made only at altitudes

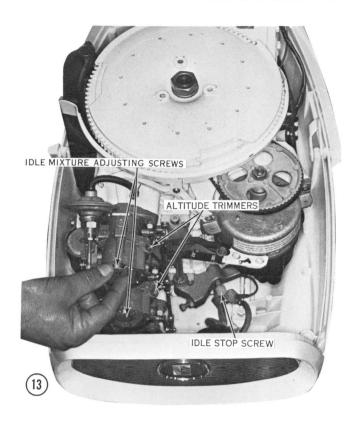

IDLE MIXTURE ADJUSTING SCREWS

ALTITUDE TRIMMERS

IDLE STOP SCREW

⑬

above 5,000'. To make the adjustment, pry out the seal over each carburetor trimmer. Hook up a tachometer and start the engine. Shift into FORWARD gear and advance the throttle to the wide-open position. Turn the trimmer adjustment clockwise (rich) until the engine speed drops, and then back it out until the speed just begins to increase and the engine runs smoothly. Repeat the adjustment to the other carburetors. *CAUTION: Operating the engine with a lean mixture will cause it to overheat, which will cause severe damage to the powerhead.*

It takes a properly tuned engine to develop the designed horsepower.

4

FUEL SYSTEM SERVICE

The 3.5 and 4 Hp engines have a fuel tank located above the engine so that the fuel is fed to the carburetor by gravity. The larger engines have a fuel pump to force the gasoline to the carburetor from a remote gas tank. A two-stage fuel pump is an integral part of the Marvel-Schebler carburetor used on the 7.5 and 9 Hp engines. The larger engines have a two-stage fuel pump (a single-stage pump is used on the 14 and 28 Hp engines) which is activated by the vacuum and pressure created in the crankcase.

These engines are equipped with either a Walbro or a Marvel-Schebler carburetor, depending on the model. Carburetor service is covered through step-by-step illustrated instructions for each model.

FUEL PUMP

The fuel pump draws fuel from the remote tank and forces it into the carburetor. The fuel pump consists of a pump body, a diaphragm, check valves, and the fuel and pressure lines. A hand-operated primer bulb, in the main fuel line from the tank, draws fuel up and forces it into the fuel pump and carburetor in preparation for starting the engine.

FUEL PUMP OPERATION

As the piston moves up and down in the cylinder bore, it creates within the crankcase vacuum and pressure that are transferred to the diaphragm of the fuel pump. This causes the diaphragm to move back and forth, drawing fuel into the pump, and then forcing it to the second stage of a two-stage fuel pump, from where it is forced into the carburetor float bowl. Check valves direct the flow of fuel towards the carburetor.

FUEL PUMP PRESSURE TEST

To check the fuel pump outlet pressure, use a 0–10 psi gauge in conjunction with a "T" fitting hooked into the main fuel pump outlet line. The accompanying specifications are for a tank in which the fuel level is 30" below the fuel pump diaphragm. If this distance is shortened, the readings will be slightly higher. *CAUTION: These specifications are not valid when the fuel surface is less than 15" below the fuel pump diaphragm.*

FUEL PUMP SPECIFICATIONS

Engine Speed (Rpm)	Outlet Pressure (Psi)				
	7.5/9 Hp	14 Hp	28 Hp	45 Hp	75 Hp
500	—	0.25	0.50	0.50	0.50
3,000	—	0.37	1.12	2.00	2.00
4,500	1.0	—	—	—	—
5,000	—	1.12	1.50	5–10	6–9

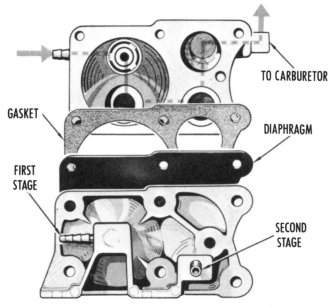

Parts of the two-stage fuel pump used on the larger engines.

FUEL PUMP, R&R

Disconnect the fuel inlet and pressure hoses. Remove the mounting screws which hold the fuel pump to the powerhead. Take off the large nylon screw, the spring, the sediment screen, and the O-ring from the lower pump body. Remove the pump body screws, and then separate the pump halves. Remove the diaphragm and gasket.

Because fuel pump pressure is dependent on the length of the hoses, always use the same length hose for a replacement.

Examine the check valves. To replace a valve, use a punch to flatten the valve case. Use a 7/16"—20 N.F. —bottoming tap to thread the inner portion of the check valve body. Insert the correct size bolt, and then tighten it until the valve is loose.

To replace a check valve, use an arbor press and a sleeve which will clear the valve cage. Start the valve into the body by hand, making sure that it is properly aligned, and then seat the valve in the pump body with the press. *CAUTION: Be careful not to damage the valve during installation.*

FUEL TANK MAINTENANCE

The fuel tank should be drained periodically and flushed with a fresh fuel mixture. If rust or varnish has formed in the tank, drain it and fill it with a nonflammable solvent. Place a handful of brass or aluminum nuts and bolts in the tank. Shake it vigorously, drain the tank, and then flush it with a fresh fuel mixture.

STORAGE

When storing a fuel tank for the winter, drain all fuel from the tank, and then clean the interior as discussed above. Allow the tank to drain thoroughly, and then coat the interior with SAE 30 motor oil. Cap the tank and store it in a clean, dry place.

In the spring, flush out all traces of the oil, using straight gasoline. Drain the oil-diluted gasoline, and then fill the tank with a fresh fuel mixture.

WALBRO CARBURETORS

Two basic types of Walbro carburetors are used; the carburetors for the smaller engines are equipped with an adjustable high-speed jet, those for the larger ones with a fixed high-speed jet and an adjustable trimmer to enrich the high-speed circuit fuel mixture for altitude.

WALBRO CARBURETOR WITH AN ADJUSTABLE HIGH-SPEED JET

3.5, 4, & 14 Hp ENGINES

The carburetors used on these smaller engines have an adjustable high-speed jet. They are basically alike in construction and operating details, but differ in jet sizes for the several applications. The idle mixture adjustment for the 14 Hp engine is an air adjustment, whereas the same adjustment for the other engines is a fuel adjustment. This means that the idle mixture adjusting screw must be turned clockwise to enrich the mixture on the 14 Hp engine, while the same adjustment for the other engines must be made in a counterclockwise direction to achieve the same result.

THEORY OF OPERATION

Fuel enters the carburetor through the fuel inlet fitting and passes through the float valve seat assembly into the fuel bowl. As the level of fuel in the bowl rises, the float valve shuts off the flow. The float valve rides on a lever attached to the float and this lever rotates on a shaft held in the carburetor body. A spring tends to hold the float up and the valve closed. The spring is overridden by the weight of the float falling as the level of the fuel in the bowl drops, and this reopens the valve.

When the engine starts, crankcase vacuum affects the fuel in the idle passage to lift it up to the idle mix-

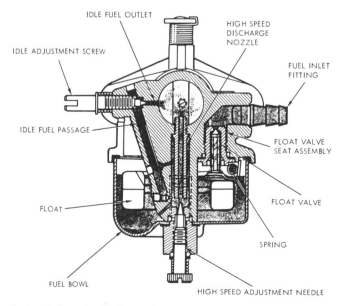

Sectioned view of a Walbro carburetor used on the smaller engines. It has both a high-speed and an idle-mixture adjusting needle.

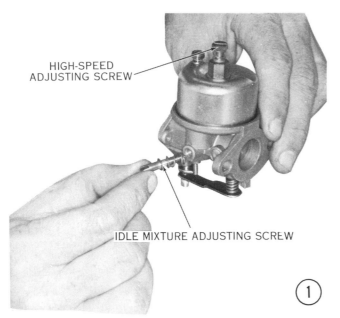

HIGH-SPEED ADJUSTING SCREW

IDLE MIXTURE ADJUSTING SCREW

①

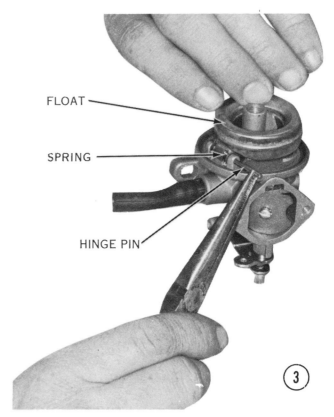

FLOAT

SPRING

HINGE PIN

③

ture adjustment screw, where it is injected into the venturi passage through the idle fuel outlet. As the throttle valve is opened, a low-pressure area is created at the venturi which results in fuel's being drawn up past the high-speed adjustment screw and through the high-speed discharge nozzle. The fuel is injected into the venturi through the main fuel outlet. The high-speed adjusting screw regulates the quantity of fuel entering the high-speed discharge nozzle.

② Remove the bowl retainer screw and the gasket under it. Take off the fuel bowl and the two gaskets; one is at the base of the carburetor, the other on the flange. Check the seating of the bowl drain valve. If necessary, depress the spring lock to take the valve apart for cleaning.

③ Remove the float hinge pin to release the float and spring.

OVERHAULING A WALBRO CARBURETOR WITH AN ADJUSTABLE HIGH-SPEED JET

DISASSEMBLING

① Remove the idle mixture adjusting screw and spring. Take out the high-speed adjusting screw, spring, and washer.

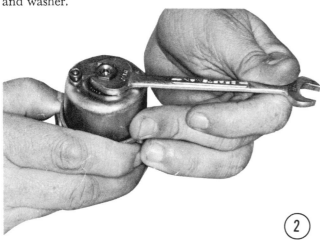

②

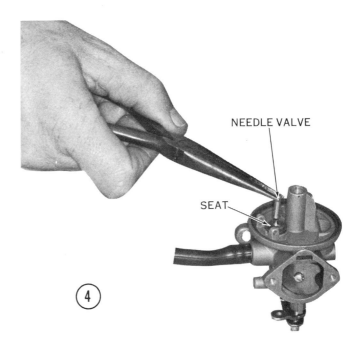

NEEDLE VALVE

SEAT

④

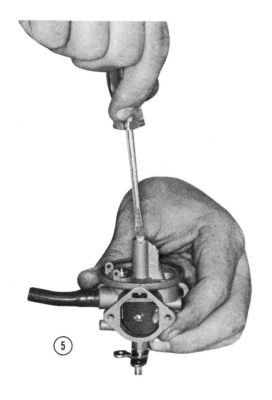

(5)

④ Take out the float needle valve and seat assembly. *CAUTION: Use a screwdriver with a blade that is wide enough to avoid burring the slot.*

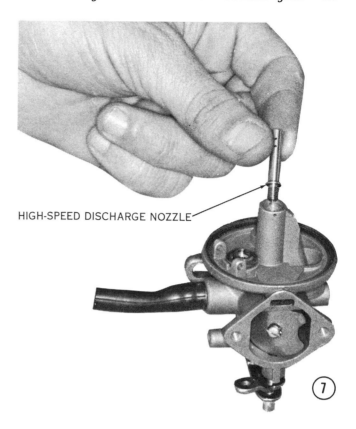

HIGH-SPEED DISCHARGE NOZZLE

(7)

⑤ Remove the high-speed discharge nozzle.

CLEANING AND INSPECTING

Clean all parts and blow them dry with compressed air. Blow compressed air through all jets, nozzles, and passageways of the carburetor body.

Always replace the needle valve and seat assembly because this is the most wearing part of the carburetor.

Check the tapered surface of the idle mixture adjusting screw to see if it is grooved, which would make an accurate adjustment difficult; if damaged, replace it.

Always replace all gaskets and O-ring seals.

ASSEMBLING

⑥ Install a new needle valve seat, using a new gasket under it. *CAUTION: Use a screwdriver with a blade wide enough to avoid burring the slot.*

⑦ Replace the high-speed discharge nozzle. No gasket is required.

⑧ Install a new needle valve, and then replace the float, float shaft, and spring. Hook the end of the spring against the body of the carburetor so that it applies tension to lift the float.

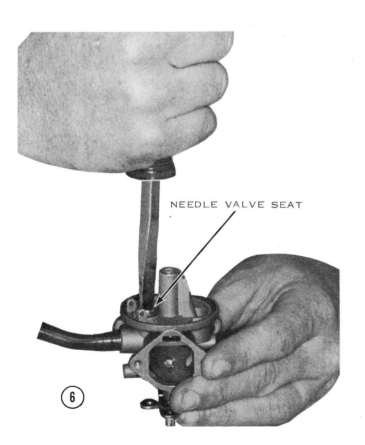

NEEDLE VALVE SEAT

(6)

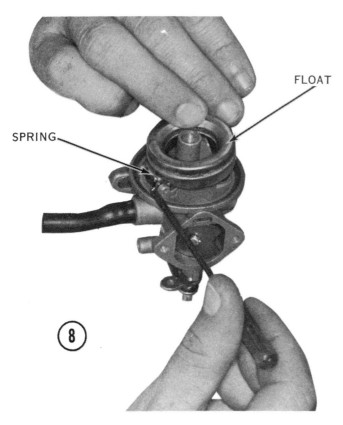

SPRING

FLOAT

⑧

⑨ Measure the float level, which should be 5/32" measured from the flange of the carburetor to the top of the float. If necessary, bend the float lip to make an adjustment.

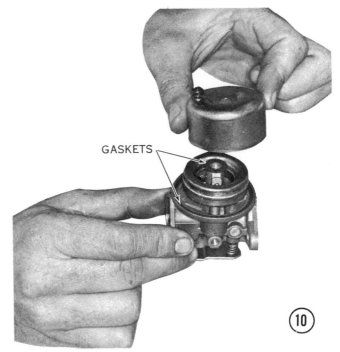

GASKETS

⑩

⑩ Position a new gasket in the groove of the flange and one on the base of the carburetor, and then replace the fuel bowl, with the drain valve facing to the left, as shown.

⑪ Install the bowl retainer screw, using a new gasket under it. Tighten the screw securely.

⑫ Replace the high-speed adjusting screw, spring, and washer. Turn the screw in (clockwise) until it seats,

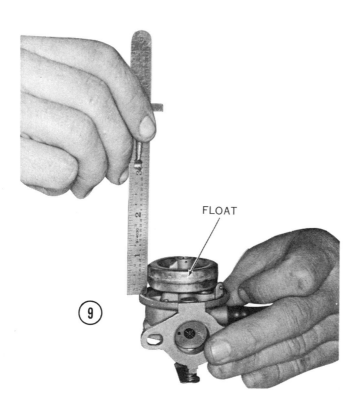

FLOAT

⑨

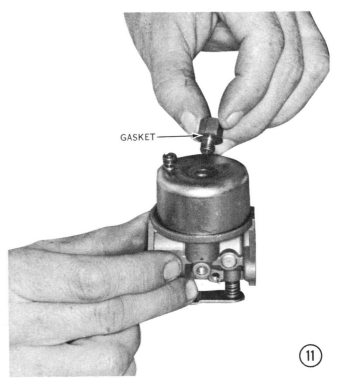

GASKET

⑪

adjustment difficult. This is a *fuel* adjustment on the 3.5 and 4 Hp engines and an *air* adjustment on the 14 Hp engine. This means that the idle mixture adjusting screw must be turned clockwise to lean the mixture on the 3.5 and 4 Hp engines and counterclockwise to lean the mixture on the 14 Hp engine.

WALBRO CARBURETOR WITH A FIXED HIGH-SPEED JET

28, 45 (since 1968) & 75 Hp Engines

The carburetors used on these engines are equipped with a fixed high-speed jet. Since 1964, the carburetors have had an altitude trimmer adjustment. One carburetor is used on the 28 Hp, two are used on the 45 Hp, and three on the 75 Hp engine. These carburetors are basically alike in construction and operating details, but differ in jet sizes for the several applications.

THEORY OF OPERATION

Idle Operation

When the engine starts, crankcase vacuum creates a suction on the fuel in the idle passage. The fuel is lifted through the idle limiting jet and up the idle fuel supply passage to the idle metering orifice. The fuel continues past the idle mixture adjusting screw and is injected into the crankcase through the idle jet. The volume of fuel

and then back it out 1-1/4 turns for a preliminary adjustment. *CAUTION: Don't force the screw into its seat, or you will damage the taper, making an accurate adjustment difficult.*

⑬ Replace the idle mixture adjusting screw and spring. Turn the screw in (clockwise) until it seats, and then back it out 1/2 to 3/4 turn for a preliminary adjustment. *CAUTION: Don't force the screw into its seat, or you will damage the taper, making an accurate*

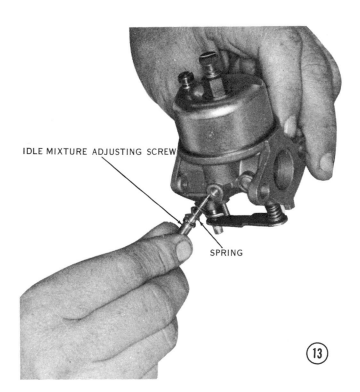

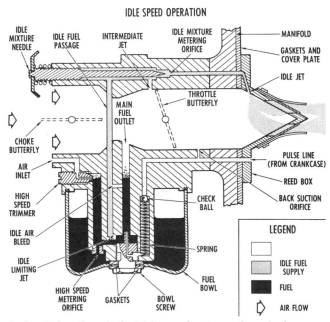

Sectioned view through the Walbro carburetor used on the larger engines. This drawing shows the flow of fuel at idle.

MID RANGE OPERATION

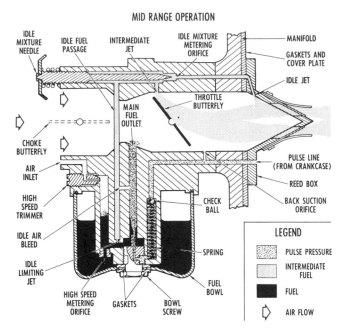

As the throttle is opened partially, fuel flows from the intermediate jet and also from the main fuel outlet in the venturi. The greater crankcase pressures are enough to unseat the spring-loaded ball check in the pulse system, thus forcing additional fuel up the main passage and into the carburetor bore.

HIGH SPEED OPERATION

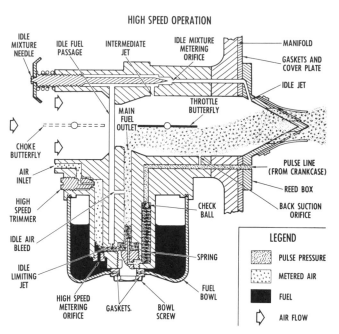

At high speeds, the pressure in the pulse system drops, and this flow of fuel is terminated. Most of the fuel is delivered through the main fuel outlet, which is located in the low-pressure area of the venturi.

passing through the idle jet is regulated by the idle mixture adjusting screw. The idle air bleed and the intermediate jet pass air into the idle system to aid in atomizing the fuel. The low pulse pressure from the crankcase during idle speed is cancelled out by the back-suction orifice, and so this system is not in operation during idle.

Mid-Range Operation

As the throttle valve is opened, fuel is expelled through the intermediate jet as well as through the idle jet. In the lower mid-range of operation, fuel is still drawn through the idle system mainly by crankcase vacuum. The intermediate jet is not metered through the idle metering orifice; therefore, a greater volume of fuel is allowed to pass through the intermediate jet. To supply the increased demands for fuel as the speed is increased, the pulse system begins to operate. The greater pressures in the crankcase are sufficient to overcome the cancelling effects of the back-suction orifice and the spring-loaded check ball. When the check ball is opened, the back pressure passes through the jet located at the bottom of the main fuel passage and forces fuel up the main passage and into the carburetor bore. The combined effects of the intermediate jet and the pulse pressure system provide the right amount of fuel for a smooth transition from idle to high-speed operation. The pulse system is effective in providing additional fuel during rapid acceleration.

High-Speed Operation

As the engine reaches high speed, the volume of air passing through the venturi becomes great enough to lower the air pressure so that fuel rises up the high-speed passage and is ejected from the high-speed outlet. As the air pressure in the carburetor drops, more fuel is drawn from the high-speed outlet. The pressures in the pulse system drop and the cycle rate of the check ball becomes such that the pulse system loses its effectiveness and less fuel is injected into the bore by this system. At high speed, a small amount of fuel will continue to be injected by the pulse system; however, the amount will be negligible. To provide further control of fuel at high speed, a trimmer adjustment can be used to tailor the fuel flow to local conditions. The trimmer bleeds air into the high-speed system to reduce the volume of fuel that passes through the high-speed outlet. As more air is bled into the system, the volume of fuel decreases. To make the trimmer adjustment, turn the screw in until it stops, and then back it out 1-1/2 turns. With the engine operating at full throttle, turn the screw to get the highest engine speed.

CAUTION: Setting the trimmer adjustment too lean can cause severe damage to the internal parts of the engine. Set the adjustment screw slightly on the rich side to provide maximum performance and protection.

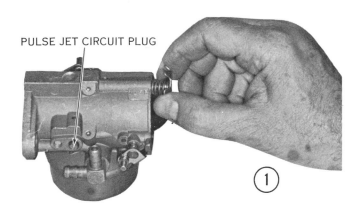

PULSE JET CIRCUIT PLUG

①

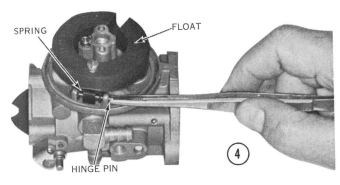

SPRING   FLOAT

HINGE PIN

④

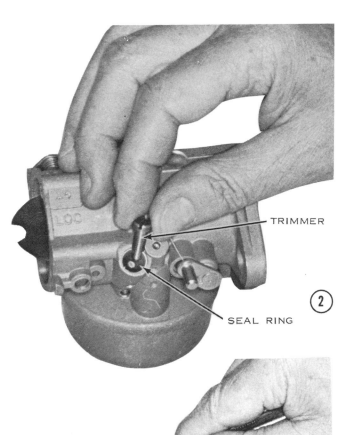

TRIMMER

SEAL RING

②

③

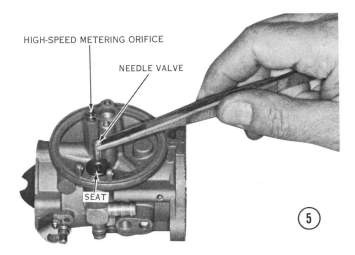

HIGH-SPEED METERING ORIFICE

NEEDLE VALVE

SEAT

⑤

OVERHAULING A WALBRO CARBURETOR WITH A FIXED HIGH-SPEED JET

DISASSEMBLING

① Remove the idle mixture adjusting screw and spring. Take out the pulse jet circuit plug.

② Pry out the lead seal, and then unscrew the high-speed trimmer. Pry the rubber seal ring from the hole.

③ Remove the bowl retainer screw, and then take off the float bowl.

④ Remove the float hinge pin. This will release the float and the spring.

⑤ Remove the needle valve and the spring. *CAUTION: Don't lose the spring.* Use a wide-bladed screwdriver to remove the needle valve seat. Take out the high-speed metering orifice.

CLEANING AND INSPECTING

Clean all parts and blow them dry with compressed air. Blow compressed air through all jets, nozzles, and passageways of the carburetor body. *CAUTION: Don't*

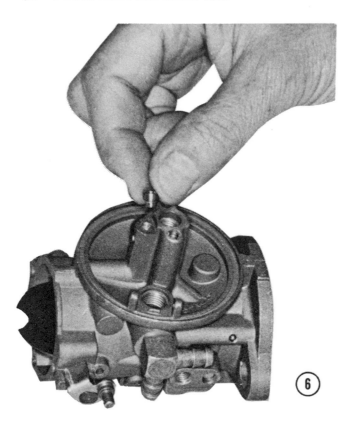

(6)

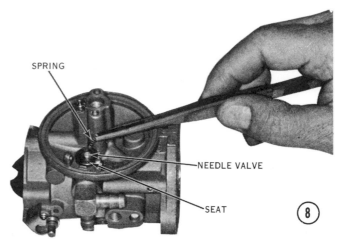

(8)

(7)

use over 10 psi pressure, or you will blow out the pulse-jet brass retaining plug. No service part is available and, if the plug is blown out, the entire carburetor will have to be replaced.

Because the pulse-jet check ball and spring cannot be removed from the body of the carburetor, inspection of this circuit poses a problem. To check this circuit, hold the carburetor with the float bowl side facing up, pour some oil into the high-speed metering orifice hole, and then blow low-pressure (10 psi) air into the bleed for this circuit on the mating flange of the carburetor. If the circuit is clear, the air pressure will unseat the ball check, and bubbles should form in the oil around the high-speed metering orifice. *CAUTION: Don't use high air pressure, or you will blow out the pulse-jet brass retaining plug.*

Always replace the needle valve and seat assembly because this is the most wearing part of the carburetor.

Check the tapered surface of the idle mixture adjusting screw to see if it is grooved, which would make an accurate adjustment difficult; if damaged, replace it.

Always replace all gaskets and O-ring seals.

ASSEMBLING

⑥ Replace the high-speed metering orifice. No gasket is used.

⑦ Replace the needle valve seat, using a new gasket under it. *CAUTION: Use a wide-bladed screwdriver to avoid damaging the screwdriver slots.*

⑧ Install the needle valve and the spring.

⑨ Replace the float. Insert the hinge pin through one ear of the carburetor body, through one ear of the float hinge, through the spring, and then through the remaining holes. *CAUTION: Make sure that the spring is installed in a way which will apply pressure to lift the float in order to close the needle valve and seat.*

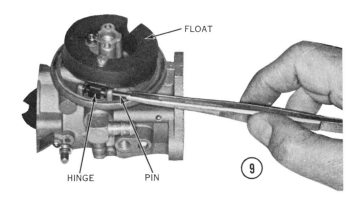

FLOAT

HINGE   PIN

(9)

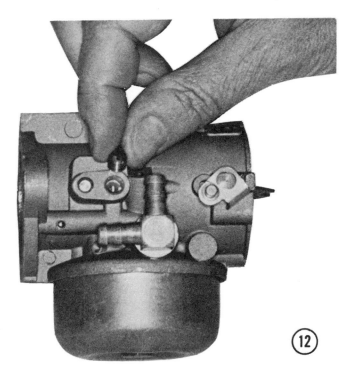

(12)

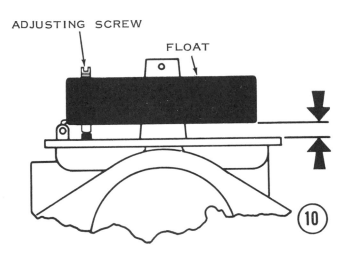

ADJUSTING SCREW

FLOAT

(10)

⑩ Measure the float level from the flange of the bowl to the top of the float. This distance should measure 5/32″.

⑪ Install a new bowl seal ring, replace the bowl, and then install the bowl retainer screw, using a new gasket under it.

⑫ Install the pulse-jet circuit plug; no gasket is needed.

⑬ Install a new seal ring in the high-speed trimmer adjustment hole.

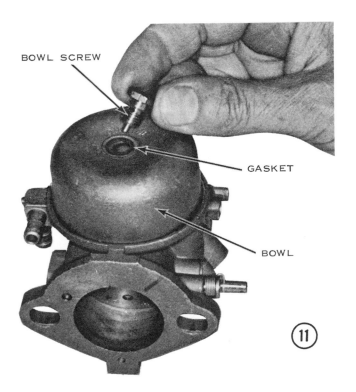

BOWL SCREW

GASKET

BOWL

(11)

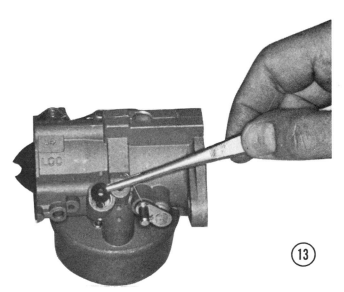

(13)

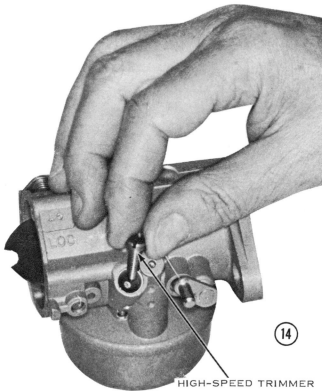

HIGH-SPEED TRIMMER

⑭ Replace the trimmer adjusting screw, and then make a preliminary adjustment by turning the adjusting screw clockwise until it lightly touches its seat, and then backing it out one full turn. *CAUTION: Don't force the needle into its seat, or you will damage the taper, making an accurate adjustment difficult to obtain.* Don't replace the trimmer adjustment lead seal until after making the final adjustment with the engine under load. These instructions are covered in Chapter 3, Tuning for Performance.

⑮ Install the idle mixture adjusting screw and spring. Turn the adjusting screw clockwise until it lightly touches its seat, and then back it out 1-1/4 turns for a preliminary adjustment. *CAUTION: Don't force the screw into its seat, or you will damage the taper, making an accurate adjustment difficult to obtain.*

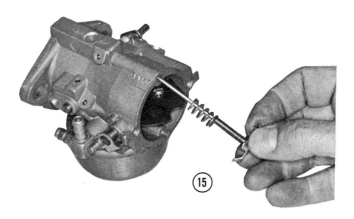

MARVEL-SCHEBLER CARBURETORS

Two different types of Marvel-Schebler carburetors are used. A single-barrel carburetor, Model SUM, with an integral, two-stage fuel pump, is used on the 7.5 and 9 Hp engines. A dual-barrel carburetor, Model VHD, was used on some 45 Hp engines.

MARVEL-SCHEBLER, TYPE VHD, CARBURETOR

45 Hp Engine

Some Model 45 engines used a single Marvel-Schebler carburetor equipped with dual venturi openings incorporated into a single body. In addition, the carburetor is equipped with an accelerator pump and an economizer system.

Fuel enters the carburetor through the inlet fitting located on the starboard side of the carburetor body, and then passes through a drilled passage until it meets with a drilled passage in the metering body. The fuel then flows through the metering body passage to the inlet seat. As the level of fuel in the bowl drops, the inlet needle opens, allowing fuel to enter the bowl. Fuel enters the metering body through the twin main jets located at the bottom of the metering body. Due to atmospheric pressure, the level of fuel in the metering body will be the same as the level of fuel in the bowl.

Idle Operation

At idle speed, the vacuum in the crankcase is transferred to the idle jet, which is located at the top of the

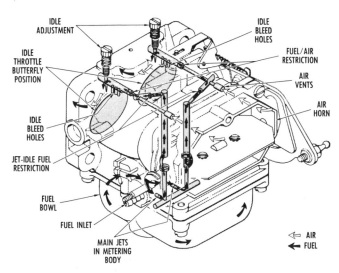

A Marvel-Schebler, Model VHD, was used on the 45 Hp engine from 1964–67. This drawing shows the flow of fuel through the idle circuit.

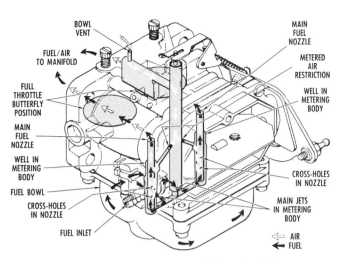

This shows the flow of fuel through the high-speed circuit.

carburetor bore on the downstream side of the throttle valve. Since the throttle valve is closed, the drawing effect at the idle jet draws fuel from the bowl, through the main jet, up through the idle transfer passage to the idle fuel jet. The fuel passes through this jet into the idle mixing chamber, where it mixes with air which is drawn through the air vent opening, located in the carburetor bore just in front of the venturi. The mixture of fuel and air then passes through the fuel/air restriction and into the next stage, where it passes through the idle jet and into the carburetor bore. The volume of fuel/air entering the bore is regulated by the setting of the idle mixture adjustment screw. The amount of fuel/air mixture which passes through the idle jet determines the idling characteristics; therefore, this adjustment is extremely important.

As the throttle valve is opened, fuel begins to flow through the idle bleed holes. Since these holes bypass the idle jet, the metering of fuel is controlled by the combined effects of the air vent opening, the idle fuel jet size, and the fuel/air restriction. At lower speeds, the volume of air passing through the venturi is not sufficient to lower the air pressure in the carburetor bore; therefore, the movement of fuel through the idle system is accomplished by the vacuum created in the crankcase.

Intermediate Operation

As the throttle valve opens, fuel is expelled through the idle and bleed openings. When the volume of air passing through the bore reaches a certain point, the air pressure in the bore drops below atmospheric pressure which is acting against the surface of the fuel in the bowl and metering body. When this occurs, the pressure against the fuel forces it up the main nozzle, where it mixes with the air passing through the bore.

High-Speed Operation

At the higher speeds, the flow of fuel through the idle and bleed openings continues but is greatly reduced, while the flow of fuel through the main nozzle increases. In addition, the economizer system begins to operate.

Economizer System

The economizer system provides a gain in fuel economy through greater control of the fuel which flows through the main metering system. The main jet orifice is calibrated so that the engine receives just the right amount of fuel at high speed. This means that the engine operates on the rich side at intermediate speeds. If the jet orifice were reduced to obtain greater intermediate speed economy, the engine would operate lean at high speed, which would result in engine damage.

The economizer system provides an additional passage through which fuel can bypass the main jets and enter the main fuel passage, which leads to the main nozzle. The passage of fuel through this system is controlled by the economizer pin and seat. From idle speeds up to approximately 3/4 throttle, the pin is seated fully and no fuel can pass through the system. The main jets, therefore, meter all the fuel. At approximately 3/4 throttle, the economizer pin begins to lift so that a small amount of fuel starts to flow through the system. This fuel is in addition to the fuel drawn through the main jets. As the speed is increased, more fuel flows through the economizer system. By carefully controlling the orifice size in the metering pin seat, and by programming the movement of the economizer pin, the carburetor is able to operate with a smaller opening in the main jets.

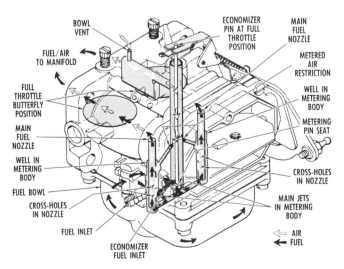

The Marvel-Schebler carburetor contains an economizer circuit. The circuit comes into operation at 3/4 throttle and adds fuel to the high-speed circuit.

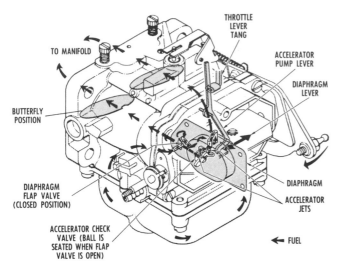

This carburetor has an accelerating circuit, consisting of a diaphragm and directional check valves. The system is operated by mechanical linkage connected to the throttle valves.

This improves low and intermediate speed economy and still provides ample fuel at high speed to keep the engine from operating lean.

Accelerating System

To prevent the engine from running lean during acceleration, the carburetor is equipped with an accelerating system. The accelerating system is operated from a diaphragm pump located on the fuel bowl, on the port side of the carburetor. As the accelerating pump lever moves out, fuel is drawn from the bowl through a flapper valve, which is a part of the diaphragm. To aid in drawing the fuel from the bowl, a check valve is installed in the accelerating system passage. This valve is seated when the flapper valve is open.

The accelerating pump lever is moved by a tang on the throttle lever. When the throttle lever is advanced rapidly, the tang on the throttle lever releases the ac-

celerating pump lever so that the spring, inside of the accelerating pump housing, pushes the diaphragm in. As the diaphragm moves in, the flapper valve closes, preventing the fuel from reentering the bowl. The fuel is forced up the passage, through the check valve, and is ejected through the accelerating jets located just in front of the venturi at the bottom of the carburetor bore. When the throttle lever is slowly advanced, the flapper valve allows enough fuel to reenter the bowl so that it is not ejected from the accelerating jets.

OVERHAULING A MARVEL-SCHEBLER, TYPE VHD, CARBURETOR

DISASSEMBLING

① Remove the idle mixture adjusting screw and the high-speed trimmer.

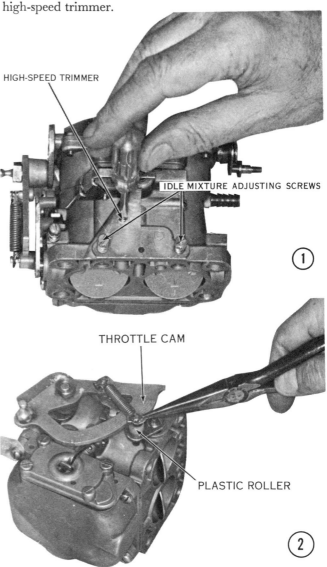

This cutaway drawing shows the parts of the accelerator circuit and their operation.

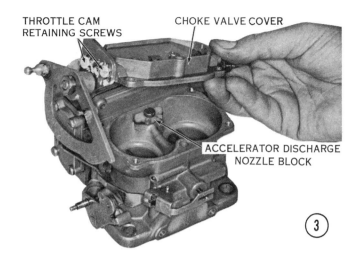

THROTTLE CAM RETAINING SCREWS

CHOKE VALVE COVER

ACCELERATOR DISCHARGE NOZZLE BLOCK

③

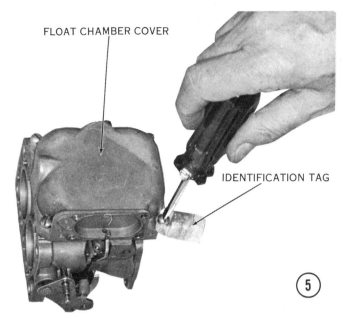

FLOAT CHAMBER COVER

IDENTIFICATION TAG

⑤

② Disassemble the throttle cam by depressing the ear of the spring retainer and then lifting up on the retainer and the spring. Disconnect the other end of the spring in a similar manner. Remove the plastic roller.

③ Remove the four screws, and then lift off the choke valve cover. *CAUTION: Don't loosen or remove the throttle cam retaining screws as this is a factory adjustment which cannot be made in the field.* Remove the accelerator nozzle block retaining screw and the block. Discard the gasket.

④ Take out the four retaining screws, and then allow the accelerating pump diaphragm cover and spring to slide over the accelerator lever. Unhook the dia-

phragm, and then remove the spring and cover. If the accelerator lever is to be removed, insert a 3/32" punch through the lower carburetor mounting flange hole to drive the roll pin out of the carburetor body.

⑤ Remove the four float chamber cover retaining screws, and then lift off the cover. Discard the gasket.

⑥ Remove the four screws holding the metering body in position, and then lift off the metering body as an assembly.

⑦ Remove the gasket. Note its position for assembly

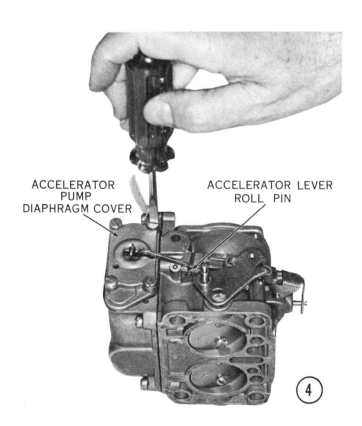

ACCELERATOR PUMP DIAPHRAGM COVER

ACCELERATOR LEVER ROLL PIN

④

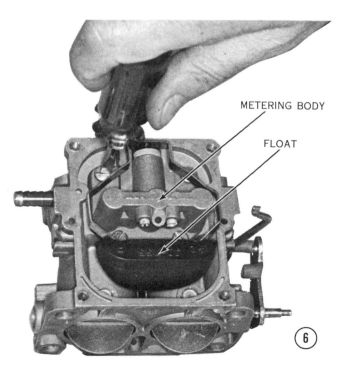

METERING BODY

FLOAT

⑥

ACCELERATOR PUMP
BALL CHECK RETAINER

ECONOMIZER PIN

⑦

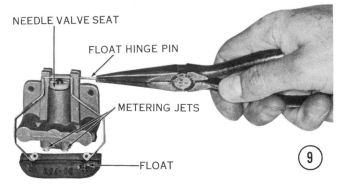

NEEDLE VALVE SEAT

FLOAT HINGE PIN

METERING JETS

FLOAT

⑨

purposes. Take out the accelerator pump ball check retainer. Turn the casting over and catch the ball check and spring, which will fall out. If the economizer pin is to be removed, use a 3/32″ punch to drive out the roll pin which holds the economizer lever to the body, and then remove the lever and spring. To remove the economizer pin, seal, and retainer from the body, pry the retaining ring out of the body, and then remove the O-ring seal.

⑧ Remove the economizer seat from the metering body.

⑨ If the float is to be removed, drive the float hinge pin out of the groove. *NOTE: Removal of the float is not desirable unless it has to be replaced.* The metering body can be cleaned by suspending it in the carburetor cleaning solution so that the float does not come into contact with the cleaner, which would destroy the plastic. To remove the needle valve and seat, tip the float assembly out of the way. Remove the metering jets.

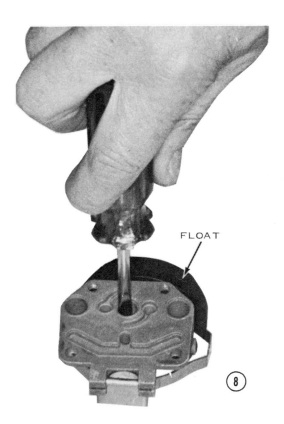

FLOAT

⑧

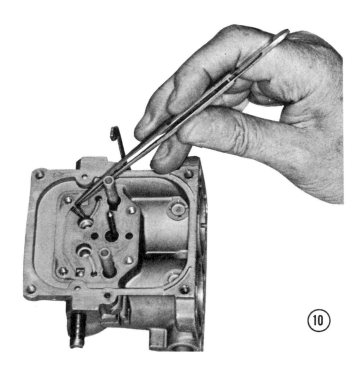

⑩

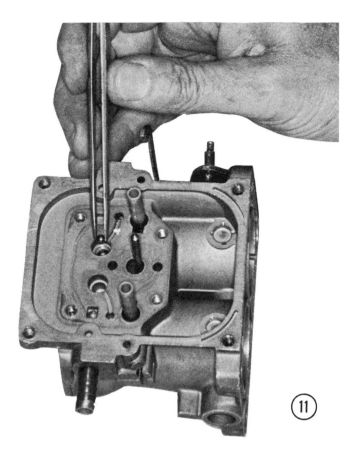

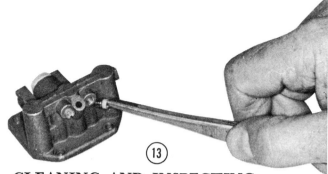

CLEANING AND INSPECTING

Clean all parts in carburetor cleaner, rinse in solvent, and then blow dry with low-pressure air. *CAUTION: Don't immerse the float assembly or the accelerator diaphragm in carburetor cleaner.* Blow low-pressure compressed air through all jets, nozzles, and passageways of the carburetor body. *CAUTION: Use air pressure which is not over 10 psi, or you may blow out a brass plug.*

Always replace the needle valve and seat assembly because this is the most wearing part of the carburetor.

Check the tapered surface of each adjusting screw to see if it is grooved, which would make an accurate adjustment difficult; if damaged, replace it.

Always replace all gaskets, diaphragms, and O-ring seals.

ASSEMBLING

⑩ Press the economizer pin through the seal ring. Install the accelerator pump check ball spring in the hole with the threads. *CAUTION: The spring must be installed with the small coil end facing up.*

⑪ Drop the ball check on top of the spring.

⑫ Insert the ball check seat. Tighten it securely.

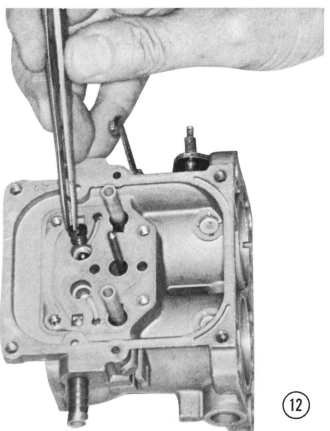

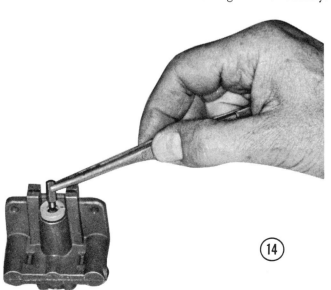

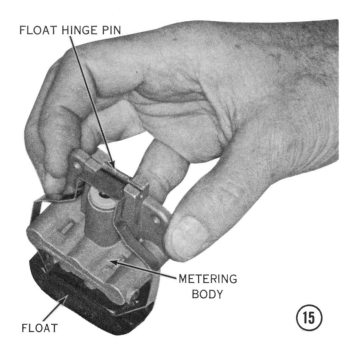

FLOAT HINGE PIN

METERING BODY

FLOAT

(15)

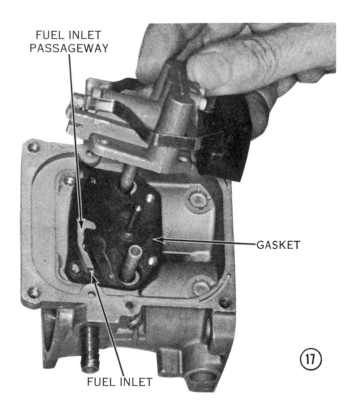

FUEL INLET PASSAGEWAY

GASKET

FUEL INLET

(17)

No gasket is required. Place the throttle body on the bench until the metering body has been assembled.

⑬ Replace the main metering jets in the metering body.

⑭ Install a new needle valve and seat assembly, using a new gasket under the seat. *CAUTION: Use a screwdriver with a blade wide enough to prevent damaging the screwdriver slots in the seat.*

⑮ Slide a new float hinge pin through the float arm, and then drive the hinge pin into the slots of the metering body only far enough to hold the float in posi-

tion. After the metering body is attached to the carburetor, the float level adjustment will be made by driving the hinge pin farther into the slots.

⑯ Replace the economizer seat; no gasket is used.

⑰ Position a new gasket on the throttle body, and

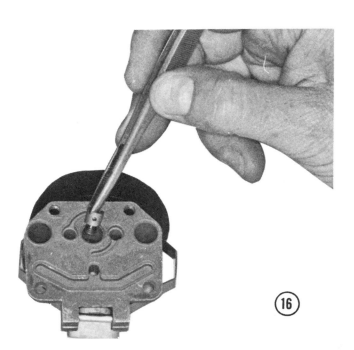

(16)

(18)

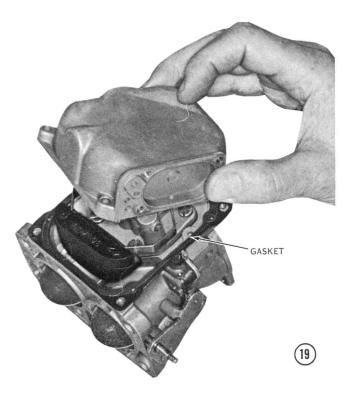

GASKET

⑲

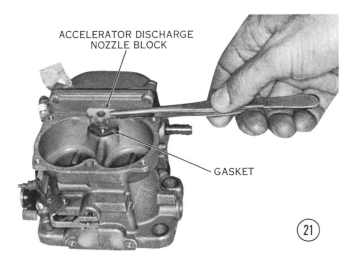

ACCELERATOR DISCHARGE
NOZZLE BLOCK

GASKET

㉑

then replace the assembled metering body. *CAUTION: Make sure that the gasket is installed properly, as shown.* Install and tighten the four short, flat-headed screws, using lockwashers under them.

⑱ To adjust the float level, hold the carburetor so that the float is at the top, and then measure the distance from the top of the float to the carburetor flange, as shown. This distance should be 15/32″. The adjustment

of the float level is determined by the distance that the float pin is depressed into the slots in the metering body. If necessary, press the pin into the slots until the specified dimension is obtained.

⑲ Position a new bowl gasket on the body, and then replace the float bowl, tightening the four retaining screws securely. *NOTE: Be sure to replace the identification tag on one of the screws.*

⑳ Slide the accelerator pump cover and spring over the accelerator pump lever, and then hook a new accelerator pump diaphragm assembly over the hook. *CAUTION: Be sure to align the flapper valve in the diaphragm with the fuel passageway in the carburetor body.* Install and tighten the four long, flat-headed screws. No lockwashers are used. Move the accelerator lever back and forth to make sure that the diaphragm moves with it.

㉑ Position a new gasket on the accelerator pump boss, and then replace the accelerator discharge nozzle block.

㉒ Install and tighten the retaining screw.

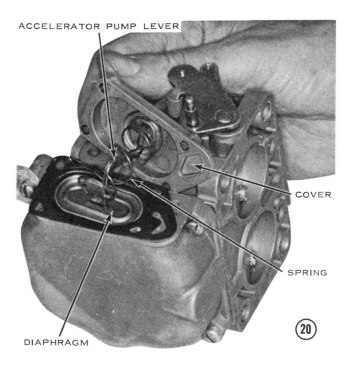

ACCELERATOR PUMP LEVER

COVER

SPRING

DIAPHRAGM

⑳

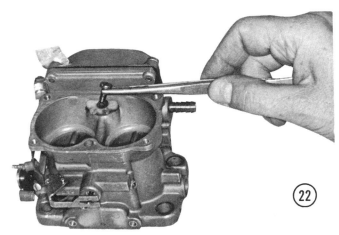

㉒

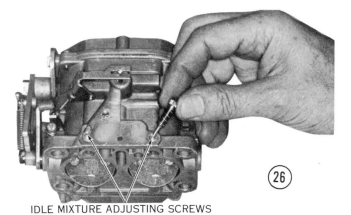

IDLE MIXTURE ADJUSTING SCREWS

㉓ Replace the choke valve cover, tightening the four retaining screws securely. No gasket or lockwashers are used. The throttle cam retaining screws are painted white to make sure that they have not been disturbed. If the paint indicates that the position of the screws has been changed, move the cam back into alignment as closely as possible, using the old lockwasher marks in the casting as a guide.

㉔ To assemble the throttle cam, install the spring in the upper pin, holding it in place with the retainer. Install the plastic roller on the throttle shaft pin, and then hook the other end of the spring and the retainer

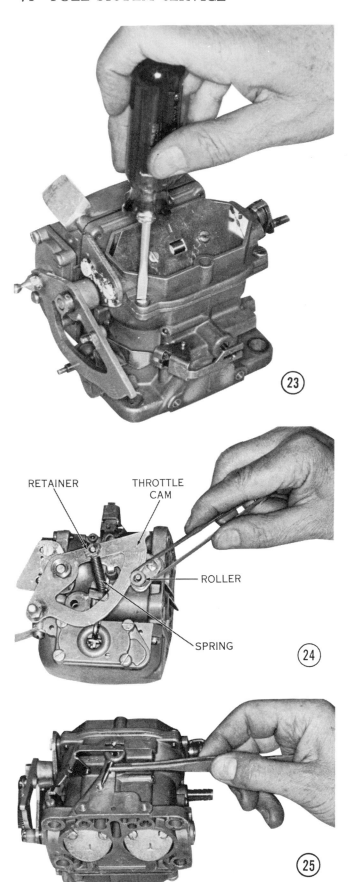

RETAINER   THROTTLE CAM

ROLLER

SPRING

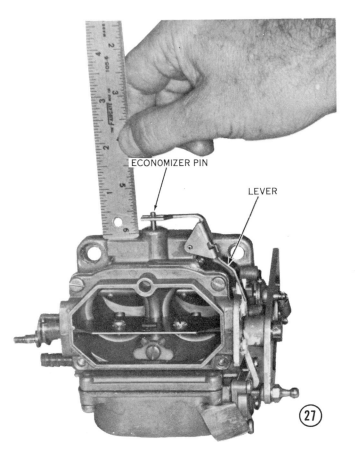

ECONOMIZER PIN

LEVER

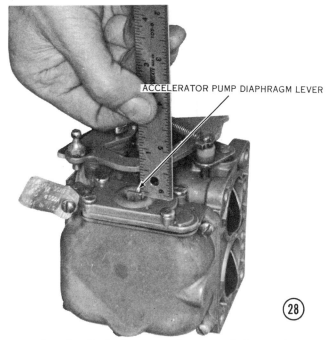

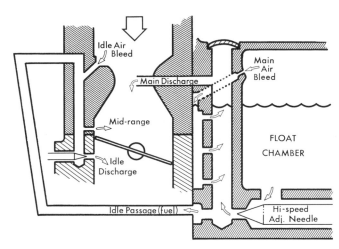

Details of the Marvel-Schebler, Model SUM, carburetor.

over the pin. Push down on the ears of the retainers to seat them in the grooves on the pins.

㉕ Install the high-speed trimmer. Turn the adjusting screw in until it lightly touches its seat, and then back it out 1-1/2 turns for a preliminary adjustment. *CAUTION: Don't force the screw into its seat, or you will groove the taper, which will make an accurate adjustment difficult to obtain.*

㉖ Replace the two idle mixture adjusting screws and springs. Turn each adjusting screw in until it lightly touches the seat, and then back it out 1 to 1-1/8 turns for a preliminary adjustment. *CAUTION: Don't force the screws into the seats, or you will groove the tapered surfaces, making an accurate adjustment difficult to obtain.*

㉗ The economizer pin must travel 1/32″–1/16″ when the throttle is moved from the closed to the wide-open position. If necessary, bend the economizer lever to make an adjustment.

㉘ The accelerator pump diaphragm lever must travel 1/16″–3/32″ when moving the throttle from the closed to the wide-open position. If necessary, bend the accelerator lever to obtain the specified dimension.

MARVEL-SCHEBLER, TYPE SUM

7.5 and 9 Hp ENGINES

In addition to the conventional carburetor circuits, this unit contains a two-stage fuel pump, operated by the pulsations in the crankcase. The crankcase pulses are controlled by flapper valves; the pressure variations are used to move diaphragms back and forth to pump the fuel from the tank to the carburetor float bowl.

OVERHAULING A MARVEL-SCHEBLER, TYPE SUM, CARBURETOR

DISASSEMBLING

① Remove the five screws holding the fuel pump cover to the throttle body. Remove and discard the gasket and fuel pump diaphragm.

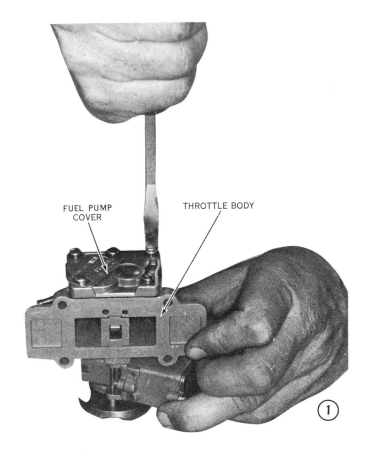

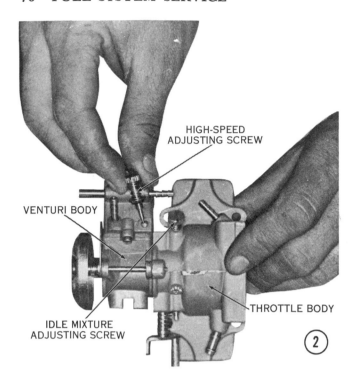

HIGH-SPEED ADJUSTING SCREW

VENTURI BODY

THROTTLE BODY

IDLE MIXTURE ADJUSTING SCREW

②

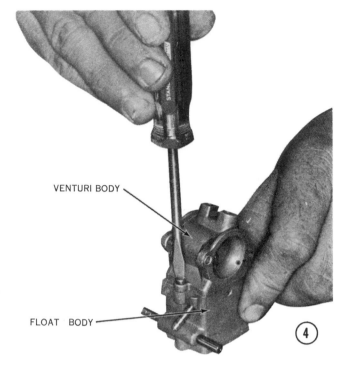

VENTURI BODY

FLOAT BODY

④

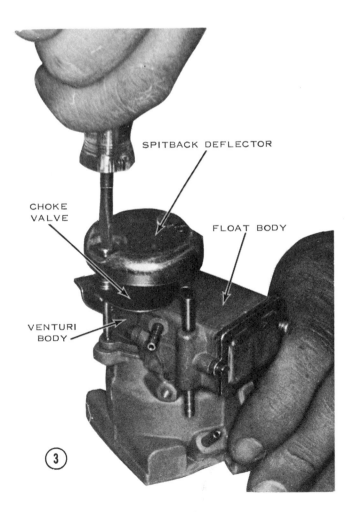

SPITBACK DEFLECTOR

CHOKE VALVE

FLOAT BODY

VENTURI BODY

③

② Remove the idle mixture and the high-speed adjusting screws. *CAUTION: Don't lose the springs.*

③ Remove the two screws holding the spitback deflector and the choke valve assembly to the venturi body. Take out the choke valve and the spring, and then lift off the float-and-venturi bodies as an assembly.

④ Remove the two screws holding the venturi body to the float body, separate the parts, and discard the gasket.

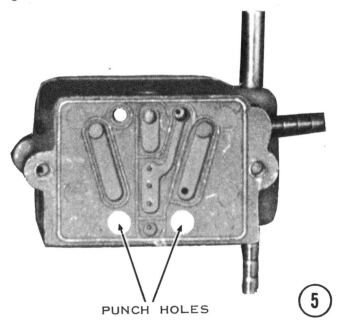

PUNCH HOLES

⑤

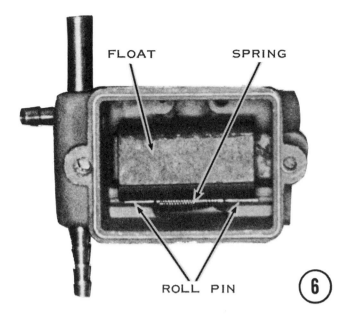

FLOAT   SPRING

ROLL PIN   ⑥

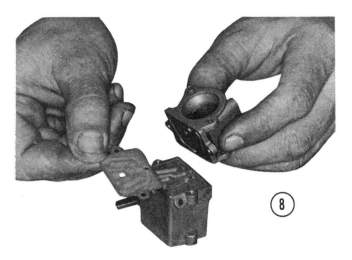

⑧

Always replace the float hinge roll pin and spring; generally they are damaged on removal.

Always replace the fuel pump diaphragm, gaskets, and O-ring seals.

ASSEMBLING

⑥ To assemble the parts of the float body, insert a new roll pin through the hinge arms on the back of the float and through the float spring. Slide the assembled float into the float chamber, making sure that the hinge arms face the bottom of the chamber. *CAUTION: Make sure that the spring is installed so that the float is spring-loaded toward the top of the float chamber.*

⑦ Press the roll pin into the slot until there is a gap of 0.115″–0.165″ between the top of the float and the top of the float chamber. *NOTE: The deeper the pin is pressed into the slot, the wider the gap becomes. If the*

⑤ Remove the float cover and discard the gasket. The float is held in place by a roll pin, which is pressed into a slot within the float chamber. To remove the roll pin, place the float chamber opening on a flat surface and use a small punch to tap the roll pin at each end. Holes are provided in the casting for this purpose. Tap on the ends of the roll pin alternately until the pin drops out of the slot. The float, roll pin, spring, and inlet needle now can be removed from the float opening side. Note the position of the spring to aid in assembling.

CLEANING AND INSPECTING

Clean all parts and blow them dry with compressed air. Blow compressed air through all jets, nozzles, and passageways of the carburetor body.

Check the tapered surface of each adjusting screw to see if it is grooved, which would make an accurate adjustment difficult to obtain; if damaged, replace it.

Always replace the needle valve and seat assembly because this is the most wearing part of the carburetor.

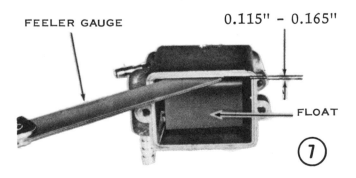

FEELER GAUGE   0.115″ - 0.165″

FLOAT   ⑦

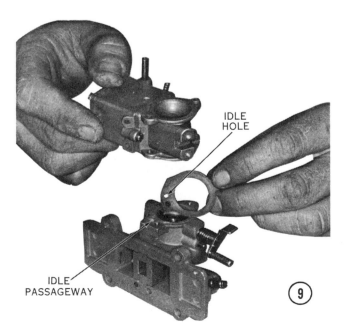

IDLE HOLE

IDLE PASSAGEWAY   ⑨

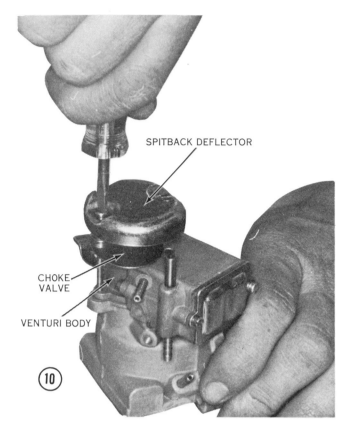

SPITBACK DEFLECTOR

CHOKE VALVE

VENTURI BODY

⑩

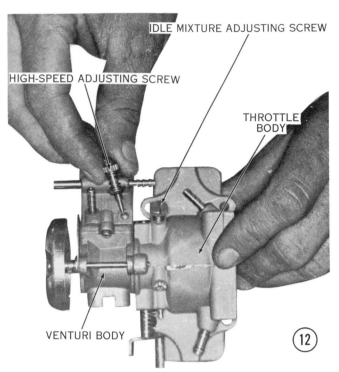

IDLE MIXTURE ADJUSTING SCREW

HIGH-SPEED ADJUSTING SCREW

THROTTLE BODY

VENTURI BODY

⑫

the two retaining screws. Position a new gasket over the float bowl, replace the cover, and then install and tighten the two retaining screws securely.

⑨ Position a new gasket on the throttle body, and then place the float-venturi assembly on the throttle body, as shown. *CAUTION: The idle hole in the gasket must match up with the idle passageway.*

⑩ Install the choke valve, spring, and spitback deflector; tighten the two retaining screws securely.

⑪ Replace the idle mixture adjusting screw (long taper) and spring. Turn it in until it seats, and then back it out 3/4 turn for a preliminary adjustment. *CAUTION: Don't force the screw into its seat, or you will damage the taper, making an accurate adjustment difficult to obtain.*

⑫ Replace the high-speed adjusting screw and

pin is pressed in too far, tap the pin back through the two holes used to remove the pin.

⑧ Position a new gasket between the float bowl and the venturi body. *CAUTION: The idle fuel port must match up with the idle passageway.* Install and tighten

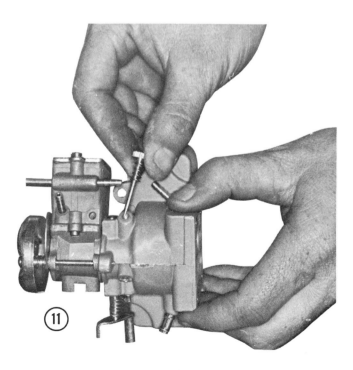

⑪

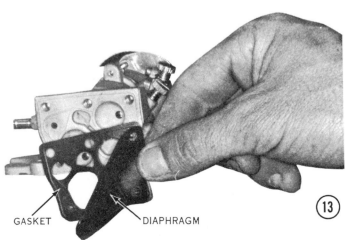

GASKET   DIAPHRAGM

⑬

spring. Turn it in until it seats, and then back it out one turn for a preliminary adjustment. *CAUTION: Don't force the screw into its seat, or you will damage the taper, making an accurate adjustment difficult to obtain.*

⑬ Install a new diaphragm and gasket on the fuel pump side of the carburetor. *CAUTION: Be sure to place the diaphragm and gasket exactly as shown.* Most models use no gasket. *CAUTION: On the models without a gasket, the diaphragm may be cut by the sharp edges on the face of the fuel pump casting unless the surface is dressed lightly on a piece of emery cloth over a flat surface.*

⑭ Replace the cover; install and tighten the five retaining screws securely.

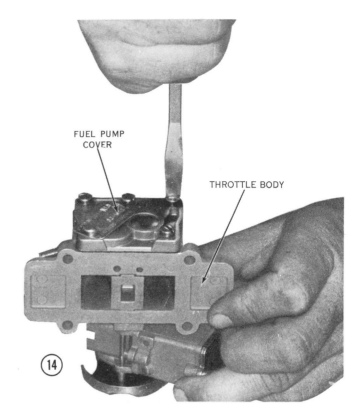

FUEL PUMP COVER

THROTTLE BODY

The boat has become an essential part of many vacations.

5

ENGINE SERVICE

Most outboard motors operate on the two-cycle principle. That is, they fire each time that the piston comes up. Most two-cycle motors have reed-type valves in place of the poppet-type used in a four-stroke cycle engine. Also, the oil must be pre-mixed with the fuel as both have to pass through the crankcase on the way to the combustion chamber.

PRINCIPLES OF OPERATION

The piston in a two-cycle motor acts as an inlet and exhaust valve. In starting a two-cycle motor, the crankshaft turns and the piston rises. Starting with the piston at its highest point of travel (and with the combustion chamber filled with a compressed mixture of air and fuel), a spark from the spark plug ignites the compressed mixture. The resulting explosion within the cylinder forces the piston down, delivering its energy to the crank shaft. During the upward stroke, the piston draws a fresh charge of fuel and air through the intake reed valve and into the crankcase. The crankcase, which is airtight, contains the crankshaft and connecting rods. On the downward stroke, the charge of fuel and air, previously drawn in, is compressed in the crankcase and, when the piston approaches the bottom of the stroke, an exhaust port is uncovered on the side of the cylinder wall. The unburned gases escape through this port, and the combustion chamber pressure falls. An instant later, the piston uncovers an inlet port on the opposite side, and the fresh charge forces its way up from the crankcase to drive out the remainder of the exhaust gases. A projection on the top of the piston, on the intake side, deflects the fresh charge and prevents it from passing directly across the cylinder and out of the exhaust port.

Recently, a new system of loop scavenging the combustion chamber has come into use. This engine has an almost flat piston dome, with a slightly curved contour. Two intake ports are slanted upward and face each other. This has a directional effect on the two incoming charges so that they impinge on each other and flow upward and around the smooth dome-shape of the combustion chamber, and then down and out of the exhaust ports on the adjacent side of the cylinder wall. The flow pattern of the fresh incoming fuel-laden gases very effectively drives out the burned gases.

On alternate-firing, twin-cylinder outboard motors, the pistons are connected to the crankshaft at a 180° angle, and a power stroke is delivered every 180°, producing the reciprocating motion which is transferred to the shaft to create the rotary motion. The firing order is governed by the magneto, which is connected to one end

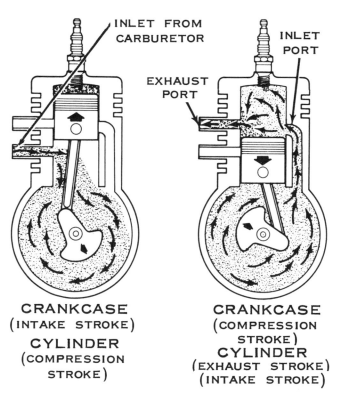

CRANKCASE (INTAKE STROKE) CYLINDER (COMPRESSION STROKE)

CRANKCASE (COMPRESSION STROKE) CYLINDER (EXHAUST STROKE) (INTAKE STROKE)

The two-stroke cycle engine fires each time that the piston comes up. Because the crankcase acts as a transfer pump for the air-fuel mixture, lubrication of the engine depends on the addition of lubricating oil to the gasoline.

of the crankshaft. At each 180° of rotation of the crankshaft, electrical sparks are generated and transmitted to
the spark plugs to fire the charges alternately. A cam,
mounted on the crankshaft within the magneto, opens
and closes the breaker points to produce these sparks.

Most two-cycle motors use reed-type inlet valves.
They operate automatically, opening when the pressure
in the crankcase is low enough so that the outside pressure can overcome the reed tension. The rate of speed
at which the engine is operating varies the crankcase
pressure and regulates the degree of opening of the reeds.
This allows a satisfactory performance level throughout
the entire speed range of the engine because the reeds
open to the varying demands created by the different
speeds.

ENGINE DETAILS

This section contains information about the disassembly, repair, and re-assembly of the one-cylinder, air-
cooled engine and the two-cylinder, water-cooled engine.
The one-cylinder engine was manufactured in a 3.5/3.6
version through 1965. A new air-cooled, 4 Hp engine was
introduced in 1965 to replace the 3.5 Hp unit. The two-
cylinder engine comes in a 7.5, 9, 14, 28, and 45 Hp
version. A three-cylinder, 75 Hp engine is also manufactured.

The material in this chapter is divided into three
sections, the first of which deals with the service pro-

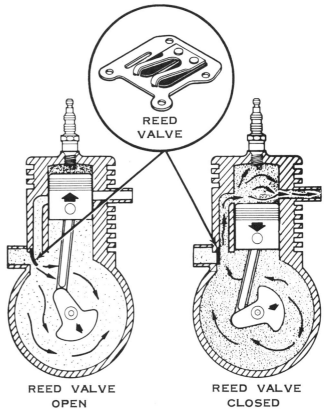

REED VALVE OPEN   **REED VALVE CLOSED**

Reed valves are used to control the flow of fuel to the crankcase. As the
piston moves upward in the cylinder, the resulting crankcase suction
overcomes the spring tension of the reed, pulling the free end from its
seat so that the air-fuel mixture can be sucked into the crankcase.

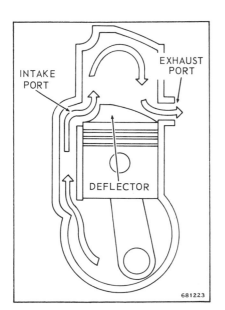 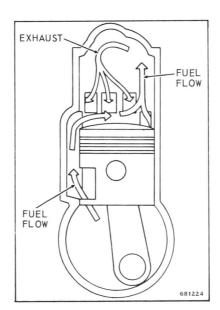 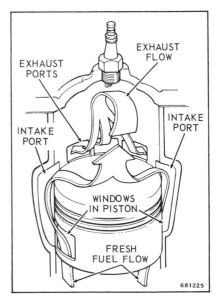

These drawings show the difference between a cross-flow type of combustion chamber (left) and the new loop-scavenged chamber (right two
drawings). In the loop-scavenged system, the piston dome is rather flat. The incoming gases are deflected across the piston by the angular direction of
the ports and drive out the exhaust gases, as shown at the right.

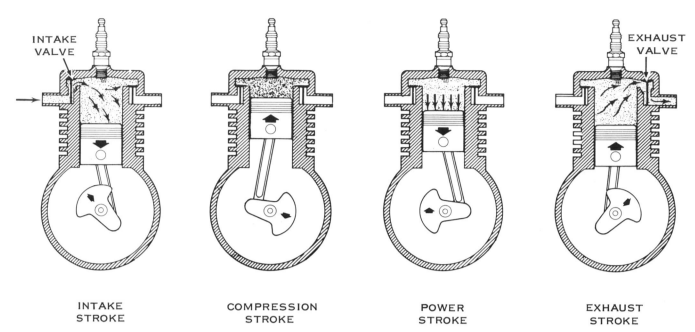

INTAKE VALVE

EXHAUST VALVE

| INTAKE STROKE | COMPRESSION STROKE | POWER STROKE | EXHAUST STROKE |

This diagram shows the four-stroke cycle gasoline engine, which fires every second time the piston reaches the top of its stroke. In other words, it takes four strokes of the piston to complete one entire cycle.

cedures for the one-cylinder engine. The second part covers the service procedures for the two-cylinder engines. The third part contains service information and exploded views to cover the three-cylinder model.

GENERAL INSTRUCTIONS

Make sure that the work bench and surrounding areas are clean before starting to work. Use clean containers to hold the parts to keep them from being lost;

biscuit tins do very nicely for screws, washers, nuts, and the other small parts. Use bread tins or coffee cans for the larger parts. Always keep replacement parts in their cartons or wrappers until ready for use. If parts are unwrapped, they are apt to get dirty, to be lost, or to be mixed with other parts which are similar.

When an engine comes into the shop for repair or overhaul, clean the exterior thoroughly. As the engine is disassembled, clean the parts in solvent and dry them with low-pressure compressed air.

TORQUE SPECIFICATIONS (IN.-LBS.)

MODELS	SPARK PLUGS	CON ROD SCREWS①	MAIN BEARING BOLTS	CRANK CASE BOLTS	CYLINDER HEAD BOLTS	FLYWHEEL NUT	POWERHEAD MOUNTING SCREWS
3.5	250	50	—	—	80	400	75–85
4	250	70–75	—	—	—	300–360	—
7.5	250	40–45	70	100	100	400③	70
9	250	40–45	70	100	100	400	70
14	250	80	80–90	80–90	80	500	80–90
28	250	180	200–225	150	150	975	80
45	250	180	300	150	220	975②	70
75	250	180	300	150	275	975	70

① With dry threads.

② Specification is for 3/8" nut. Tighten 35/64" nut to 1,500 in.-lbs.

③ Early 7.5 and 9 Hp electric-start engines use an armature retaining screw with three raised ridges. This screw should be tightened to 225 in.-lbs. of torque. Later-production screws, with six raised ridges, should be tightened to 300 in.-lbs.

MECHANICAL ENGINE SPECIFICATIONS

MODEL	CYL.	YEAR	HORSE-POWER (Hp at Rpm)	BORE & STROKE (Inches)	DISPLACE-MENT (Cu. In.)	OVERSIZE PISTON Size	Part No.	OVERSIZE BORE (Inches)	FULL-THROTTLE RANGE (Rpm)	CRANKSHAFT END PLAY (Inches)
3.5	1	1963-65	3.5 @ 3,500	2-1/8 x 1-3/4	6.23	—	—	—	3,100-3,900	—
3.6	1	1960-62	3.6 @ 4,000	2-1/8 x 1-3/4	6.23	—	—	—	3,600-4,400	—
4.0	1	1965-68	4.0 @	2-1/2 x 1-1/2	5.3	.030	81619	2.1560-2.1570	3,400-4,000	—
7.5	2	1960-68	7.5 @ 4,500	1-15/16 x 1-11/16	10.0	.020	80491	1.9570-1.9580	4,200-4,800	—
9	2	1966-68	9 @ 5,500	1-15/16 x 1-11/16	10.0	.020	80761	1.9570-1.9580	4,800-5,800	—
12	2	1960-61	12 @ 4,800	2-1/4 x 2-1/16	16.4	.030	80492	2.2800-2.2810	4,400-5,200	—
14	2	1962	14.1 @ 5,000	2-1/4 x 2-1/16	16.4	.030	80492	2.2800-2.2810	4,600-5,400	—
25	2	1960	25 @ 4,800	2-51/64 x 2-7/16	29.97	.030	80493	2.8250-2.8260	4,400-5,200	—
28	2	1961-68	28 @ 5,000	2-51/64 x 2-7/16	29.97	.030	80493	2.8250-2.8260	4,400-5,200	—
40	2	1960	40 @ 4,800	3-1/8 x 2-3/4	42.18	.030	78977A	3.1550-3.1560	4,400-5,200	.000-.002
43	2	1961-62	43.7 @ 5,000	3-1/8 x 2-3/4	42.18	.030	78977A	3.1550-3.1560	4,600-5,400	.000-.002
45	2	1963-68	45 @ 5,200	3-1/8 x 2-3/4	42.18	.030	78521①	3.1550-3.1560	4,800-5,600	.000-.002
60	3	1960	60 @ 4,800	3-1/8 x 2-3/4	63.27	.030	78977A	3.1550-3.1560	4,400-5,200	.008-.010
75	3	1961-68	75.2 @ 5,200	3-1/8 x 2-3/4	63.27	.030	78521	3.1550-3.1560	4,800-5,600	.008-.010

① Use 78977A on Models 65304510, 65304520, 65304530 (1965).

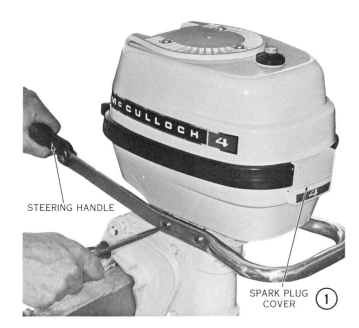

STEERING HANDLE

SPARK PLUG COVER ①

OVERHAULING A ONE-CYLINDER, 4 HP AIR-COOLED ENGINE

DISASSEMBLING

① Remove the four retaining screws, and then take off the steering handle. Snap out the spark plug cover, and then take out the two retaining screws.

② Remove the four retaining screws, pull out the front panel, and then pry the choke rod from the choke lever with a screwdriver.

CHOKE LEVER   ②

③ Remove the three retaining screws, and then lift out the starter assembly.

④ Take out the four retaining screws, and then lift off the skirt.

⑤ Remove the fuel tank by disconnecting the fuel line and draining the fuel into a clean container. Close the fuel shut-off valve, take out the four retaining screws, and then lift off the tank.

FUEL SHUT-OFF VALVE

⑥ Remove the spark plug. *CAUTION: Support the rear of the socket to keep it from tilting, which would crack the porcelain.* Remove the flywheel. Keep it from turning by inserting a screwdriver against the special reinforced boss, as shown. If the flywheel is tight, use a puller to remove it. Attach the puller to the three holes in the flywheel, and then rap the center bolt of the puller sharply with a mallet until the flywheel breaks loose from the crankshaft.

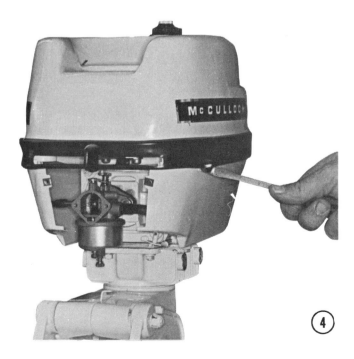

BOSSES

FLYWHEEL

CAM
CRANKSHAFT
HIGH-TENSION WIRE

⑦

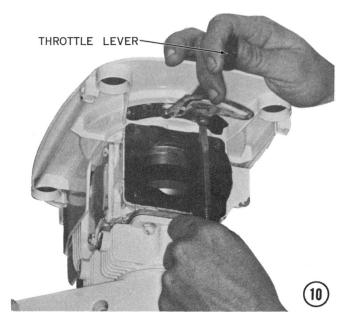

THROTTLE LEVER

⑩

INTAKE MANIFOLD

CARBURETOR

⑧

INTAKE
MANIFOLD

STOPS

REED VALVE

⑨

⑦ Lift off the breaker cam. Pry out the Woodruff key. Disconnect the high-tension wire at the attachment to the cylinder.

⑧ Remove the two retaining nuts, and then take off the carburetor. Remove the four retaining screws, and then take off the intake manifold. *CAUTION: Be careful not to bend the reed valves under the manifold.*

⑨ Remove the two retaining screws, and then lift off the reed valves and stops. *CAUTION: Handle them with care to keep from damaging or bending the parts.*

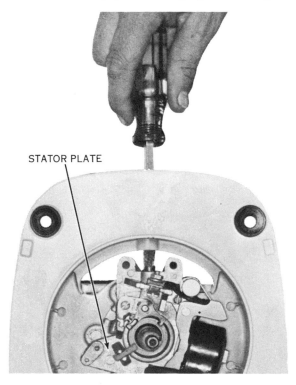

STATOR PLATE

⑪

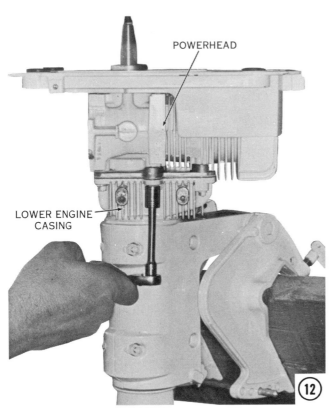

POWERHEAD

LOWER ENGINE CASING

⑫

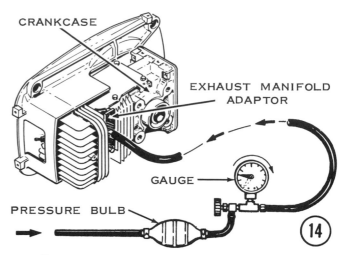

CRANKCASE

EXHAUST MANIFOLD ADAPTOR

GAUGE

PRESSURE BULB

⑭

⑩ Remove the throttle lever which also serves as a magneto lever.

⑪ Remove the friction adjustment screw, and then lift off the stator plate assembly.

⑫ Take out the six retaining capscrews, and then lift the powerhead from the lower engine casing.

⑬ To disassemble the powerhead, take off the exhaust pipe and the adaptor plate.

⑭ Before removing the exhaust manifold, test the crankcase for air leaks, which might be hard to find after the engine is disassembled. To test for an air leak, temporarily replace the spark plug and install a hose from the pressure side of the gauge (P/N 62158) to the exhaust port adaptor. Open the shut-off valve. Pump up pressure until the gauge reads 5–6 psi. Close the shut-off valve. Submerge the crankcase assembly in a tank of solvent to check for air bubbles. *NOTE: A leakage rate of one psi or less per minute is considered normal and will not affect engine performance.*

⑮ Take out the six capscrews, and then lift off the crankcase cover plate.

⑯ Remove the transfer port cover.

⑰ Turn the crankshaft until the piston is at bottom dead center, which will position the connecting rod cap

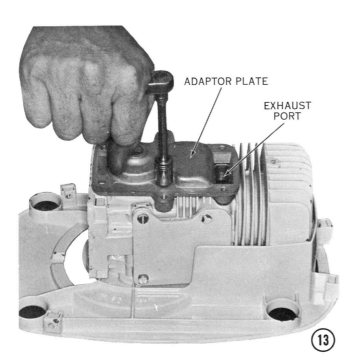

ADAPTOR PLATE

EXHAUST PORT

⑬

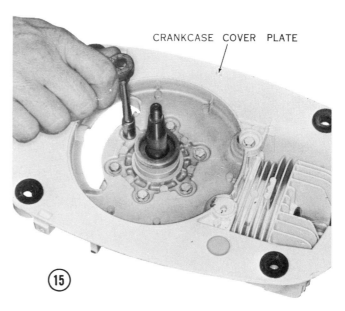

CRANKCASE COVER PLATE

⑮

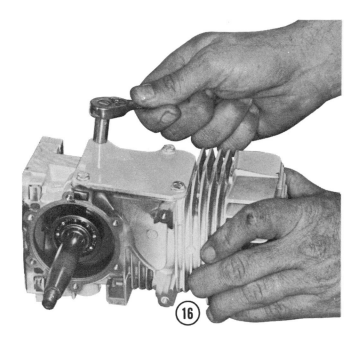

NEEDLE BEARING

(19)

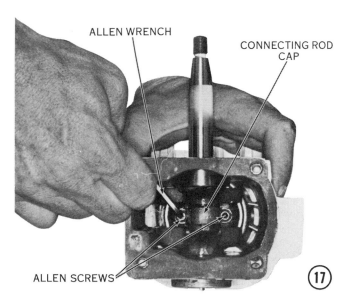

ALLEN WRENCH

CONNECTING ROD CAP

ALLEN SCREWS

(17)

at the best place to remove the two Allen screws. Lift off the cap. *CAUTION: Keep from dropping the roller bearings.*

⑱ Turn the crankshaft to push the piston to the top of the bore, reverse the crankshaft rotation, and then slide it out of the crankcase. Take out the connecting rod roller bearings. *CAUTION: When removing the crankshaft, make sure that the counterweights do not hang up on the end of the connecting rod, which would damage the rod severely.* Press the ball bearing off the crankshaft, if necessary.

⑲ Lift the piston and rod assembly out of the cylin-

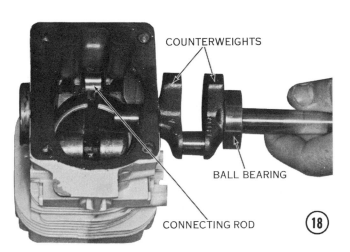

COUNTERWEIGHTS

BALL BEARING

CONNECTING ROD

(18)

PRESS

PISTON

(20) CONNECTING ROD

der. Pull the needle bearings from the crankcase, if necessary.

⑳ Remove the old piston rings. Heat the piston with a heat lamp to approximately 300°F., concentrating the heat around the closed-end bearing portion of the piston skirt. Press the piston pin, along with the closed-end bearing, from the piston. *CAUTION: Unless the piston is heated enough to release the closed-end bearing, it will be damaged by forcing it out.*

CLEANING AND INSPECTING

Examine the crankcase-cylinder assembly carefully for cracks and damaged gasket surfaces, both inside and out. Check the bearing bore for scoring, gouging, wear, and out-of-round. Replace the crankcase assembly if the bore shows evidence of bearing seizure or galling.

Examine the cylinder bore for scores. If cracks or severe scoring is found, the crankcase-cylinder assembly must be replaced. This, of course, also requires a new piston and rings. A moderately scored cylinder can be rebored 0.030″ oversize. Oversize pistons and rings are available for service. Always check the cylinder bore for an out-of-round condition. Use a dial indicator to determine the amount of cylinder bore wear. Take readings at different points around the cylinder bore to indicate the degree of out-of-round.

Taper is found by positioning a dial indicator at the top and then at the bottom of the ring-travel area. The difference between the top and bottom readings is the amount of taper in the cylinder bore.

Taper also can be measured with a new piston ring, if a dial indicator is not available. To use a piston ring for this purpose, place it into the cylinder bore; use a piston to square it with the cylinder bore. Measure the ring end gap at the bottom of the cylinder and record the measurement. Now push the ring to the top of the cylinder, again using the piston to keep the ring square, and then measure the end gap in the new position. The gap at the top of the cylinder will be greater because of the taper, and the difference between the reading at the top of the cylinder and that at the bottom is the amount of taper.

If the taper or out-of-round measurement exceeds 0.005″, the cylinder should be rebored and honed and an oversize piston and rings installed. Reboring or honing will clear up cases of scoring, if the scores are not too deep.

Always measure a rebored cylinder and the diameter of the oversize piston to be installed. Measure the piston just below the lower ring groove. The correct sidewall clearance should be 0.0025″–0.0035″.

After a cylinder has been rebored or honed, it must be cleaned thoroughly. Swab the inside of the cylinder with a rag soaked in SAE 10 oil, and then wipe it out with a clean, dry cloth. Repeat the swabbing and wiping several times until a clean cloth shows no dirt or discoloration. *CAUTION: Don't use gasoline or solvent to clean the cylinder bore because these liquids cannot remove the abrasive which is left on the cylinder walls after honing. If allowed to remain, the abrasives will cause very rapid wear on the cylinder walls and on the piston and rings, and this will result in a greatly shortened engine life.*

Proper cleaning of the cylinder walls and ports is exceedingly important. Use a wire brush or a wooden scraper to remove the carbon deposits in and around the exhaust ports. Clean the ports with a cloth soaked in SAE 10 oil, and then wipe the surface dry with a clean cloth. Clean the cylinder bore in the same way.

Piston and Piston Pin

Examine the piston carefully for a scuffed or scored skirt or cracked or distorted ring lands. Discard the piston if any such defect is found. To clean the piston, soak it

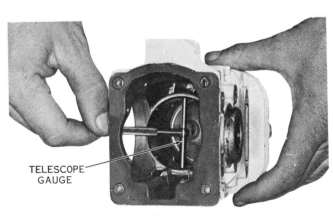

Measure the diameter of the cylinder barrel in several places to determine whether it is worn or tapered.

Measure the diameter of the piston just below the ring lands to determine the amount of wear.

To measure the piston ring end gap, push a new piston ring into the cylinder bore, square it up with an inverted piston, and then measure the gap with a feeler gauge.

Use the broken end of a piston ring to scrape the carbon from the ring grooves. CAUTION: Be careful not to nick the sides of the ring grooves, which are the sealing surfaces for the new ring.

in solvent to loosen the carbon in the ring grooves. Remove the carbon with a ring groove scraper, which can be made by breaking an old piston ring and filing one end square for a scraping edge. *CAUTION: Be careful not to nick the ring groove side walls, as these are sealing surfaces. CAUTION: Never buff the piston with a wire brush.* Rinse the piston in solvent and wipe it clean with a dry cloth.

Examine the piston pin for wear and replace it if any wear is noted. Always replace the pin if a new piston is to be installed.

Piston Rings

Always replace the piston rings whenever the engine is disassembled for service. Even though the rings appear to be in good condition, they have been subjected to wear, pressure, and constant tension. In addition, they can take a permanent set if the engine has been severely overheated.

To fit a new set of piston rings, push the new ring down into the bore of the cylinder with an inverted piston to make sure that the ring is square with the cylinder bore. The ring should be positioned just above the exhaust ports. Measure the ring end gap, which should be 0.008"–0.012". If the end gap is less than

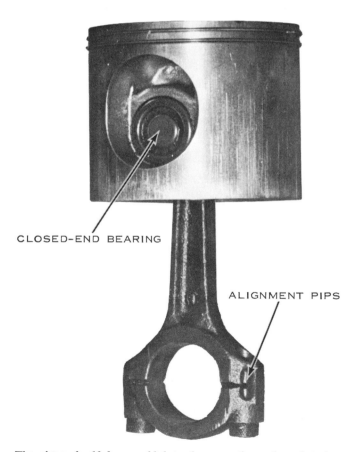

The piston should be assembled to the connecting rod so that the closed end bearing is on the same side as are the alignment pips.

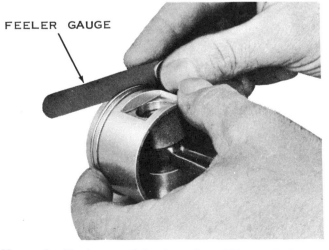

Measure the side clearance of the piston ring, which must be 0.0015–0.004".

0.008", file the ends until the correct gap is obtained. Repeat the process with the second ring. *CAUTION: If the end gap is less than 0.008", expansion will cause the ends to butt together, causing cylinder wall scuffing and possible seizure.*

To check the side clearance of the piston rings in the grooves of the piston, place a new ring in each groove. Rotate the rings all around the grooves to make sure that they are free. Use a feeler gauge to check the side clearance between the rings and the grooves, which should be 0.0015"–0.0040". If the clearance is more or less than specifications, replace the piston.

Two-cycle engine piston rings are especially designed for this type of service. Some of them have low out-

ward pressure at the ring ends so that there can be no tendency for the ends to hang up in the cylinder ports. *CAUTION: Using an improperly designed ring will result in piston ring breakage and cylinder wall scoring.*

Connecting Rod

Clean and examine the connecting rod for damage and wear. Look for scores on the bearing surfaces and twisting or bending of the rod.

Crankshaft

Examine the crankshaft bearing surfaces for scoring and galling. Look for a worn keyway, a sheared key, or stripped threads. Any burrs should be dressed down care-

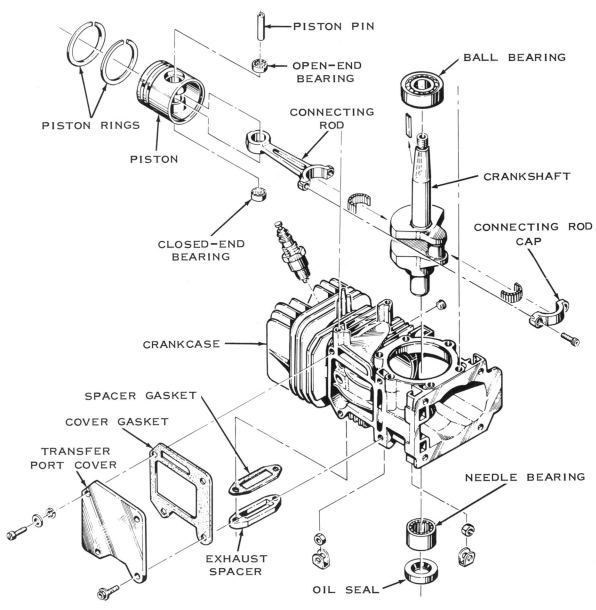

Exploded view of the 4.0 Hp engine.

THE BEARING
AND PISTON BOSS
MUST BE EVEN

㉑

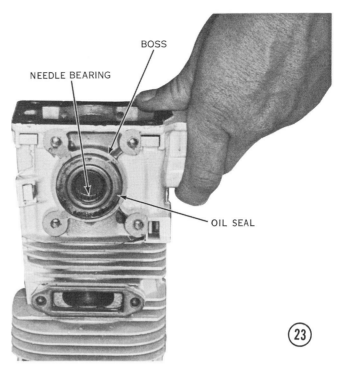

NEEDLE BEARING

BOSS

OIL SEAL

㉓

fully with a fine file and then polished with crocus cloth. If the crankshaft is worn or damaged, it should be replaced. *CAUTION: It is more economical to replace a damaged crankshaft than it is to repair it.* A poor repair job may result in damage to other parts of the engine, which would cause greater expense than a new crankshaft.

Bearings

Inspect ball bearings for abnormal wear and flat spots. Wash the bearing in gasoline or solvent and revolve it by hand to test for roughness. *CAUTION: Never spin a ball bearing with compressed air or you will damage the races.* After washing, lubricate the bearing with clean oil.

Inspect needle bearings for wear and for burned or flattened rollers. Discard any defective bearings. The 24 connecting rod needle bearings should be replaced as a set if any are damaged, worn, or burned.

Oil Seals

Examine the oil seals and gaskets thoroughly for cuts and wear. Always replace all oil seals because of the possibility of air leaks and a crankcase pressure loss.

Clean the crankcase cover thoroughly with solvent, removing all dirt and foreign material. Inspect the gas-

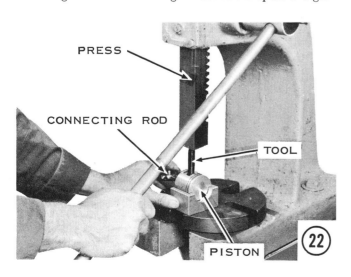

PRESS

CONNECTING ROD

TOOL

PISTON

㉒

ket surfaces for burrs, which might cause difficulty in sealing. Clean the crankcase cover gasket surfaces thoroughly. Examine the screw hole threads. If the threads are stripped, make a repair with a Heli-Coil insert.

Reed Valves

Inspect the reed-valve plate assembly for defects. The reed valves must lie flat against the reed plate and they must cover the openings fully. Any gap will result in leakage and poor engine performance.

ASSEMBLING

㉑ Hold the piston under a heat lamp or in an oven until it reaches approximately 300°F. Place the closed-end ball bearing (with the shield side facing out) into the bearing boss of the exhaust port side of the piston. Press the bearing into the piston boss so that the inside edge of the bearing is flush with the boss. Press the open-end bearing into the other side of the piston until the inside edge of the bearing is flush with the inside edge of the boss.

㉒ Heat the connecting rod to approximately 300°F. Lightly oil the piston pin and bearing rollers. Insert the piston pin through the open-end bearing. Insert the connecting rod into the piston, and then press the pin through the connecting rod and piston. *CAUTION: Don't press the piston pin below the surface of the open-end bearing. If the pin touches the shield of the closed-end bearing, friction will destroy the bearing and cause*

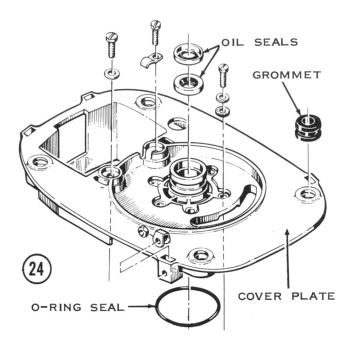

OIL SEALS

GROMMET

(24)

O-RING SEAL

COVER PLATE

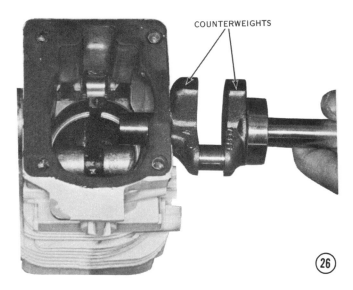

COUNTERWEIGHTS

(26)

serious damage. If the piston pin is pressed into the closed-end bearing too far, both the pin and the closed-end bearing will have to be pressed out of the piston. Usually, when this is done, the piston pin will be distorted or the shield of the closed-end bearing will be broken, in which case parts will have to be replaced.

㉓ Heat the crankcase to approximately 180°F.,

concentrating the heat as much as possible in the area of the lower bearing bore. Press the needle bearing into the bearing bore until the outer edge of the bearing is about 1/8″ inside of the seat for the oil seal. Install the oil seal. *NOTE: The outside face of the oil seal must be flush with the face of the boss.* Press the ball bearing onto the crankshaft.

㉔ Heat the crankcase cover plate to approximately 180°F., and then press the two oil seals into the cover plate. *NOTE: These seals go in back to back, the lower*

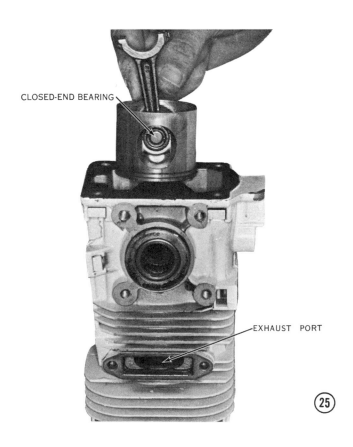

CLOSED-END BEARING

EXHAUST PORT

(25)

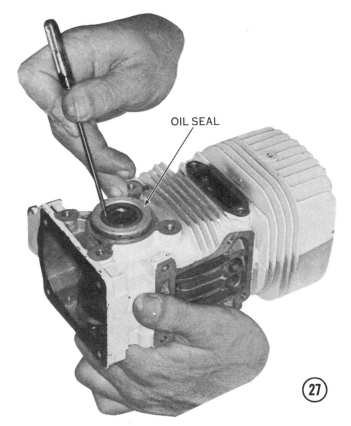

OIL SEAL

(27)

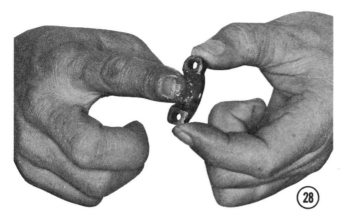

(28)

(30)

one with the lips facing down and the other with the lips facing up. Later models use one seal which must be installed with the lips facing down. Then press the crankshaft ball bearing into the cover plate. Install the O-ring seal on the crankcase cover plate.

㉕ Install the rings on the piston, using a ring expander to avoid a permanent set. Make sure that the end gaps are over the pins. Oil the piston and rings and the inside of the cylinder bore with a light coat of engine oil. Insert the piston and connecting rod assembly (with the cap removed) into the cylinder bore. *CAUTION: Make sure that the closed-end bearing in the piston is facing the exhaust port side of the cylinder.*

㉖ Insert the crankshaft into the crankcase. Turn the crankshaft until the counterweights are in position to slide past the connecting rod end.

㉗ Use a small screwdriver to spread the oil seal ring around the crankshaft as you slide it into position.

㉘ Coat the connecting rod needle bearing surfaces with a non-fiber type grease.

㉙ Place 12 needle bearings in both the rod and cap, holding them in position with the grease. *NOTE: If a new set of bearings is purchased, it will be found that the package contains 25 needle bearings; only 24 are needed.*

㉚ Work the connecting rod into position around the crankpin, and then attach the connecting rod cap. Make sure that the pips on the rod and cap are together and that the cap fits tightly around the crankpin. *CAU-*

TION: If the cap is assembled in reverse, the fractured edges will not match. If the screws are tightened, the fractured projections will be distorted, rendering the rod and cap useless. Lubricate the connecting rod screws, and then insert them into the connecting rod cap. Torque the screws to 70–75 in.-lbs. Rotate the crankshaft through several revolutions to make sure that it turns freely.

㉛ Replace the transfer port cover, using a new gasket to seal the opening. Tighten the retaining capscrews securely.

(31)

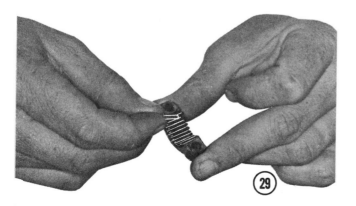

(29)

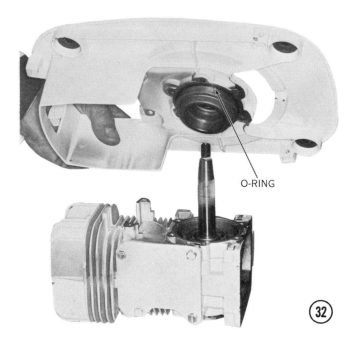

O-RING

③②

㉜ Make sure that the new O-ring seal is in position in the crankcase cover plate, and then install the plate on the crankcase-cylinder assembly. Tighten the six cap-screws securely.

㉝ Replace the exhaust port adaptor plate, using a new gasket between the adaptor and the cylinder.

㉞ Install and tighten the single retaining capscrew as shown, position a new gasket on the adaptor plate, and then replace the exhaust pipe. Install and tighten the retaining screws securely.

㉟ Install and tighten the one capscrew which holds the exhaust pipe to the adaptor plate. *CAUTION: Make*

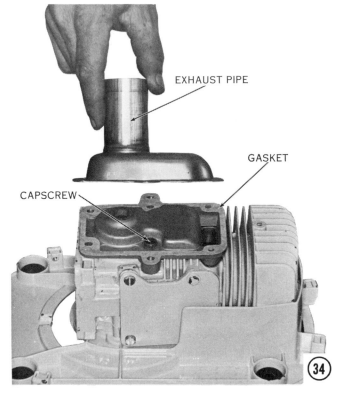

EXHAUST PIPE

GASKET

CAPSCREW

㉞

sure that the other holes in the adaptor plate are aligned with the holes in the cylinder, because these bolts have to be installed after the powerhead is in position on the lower engine casing.

㊱ Position a new gasket on the lower engine casing, and then install the assembled powerhead. *NOTE: It may be necessary to turn the crankshaft to line up the splines.* Tighten the retaining capscrews securely.

GASKETS

㉝

㉟

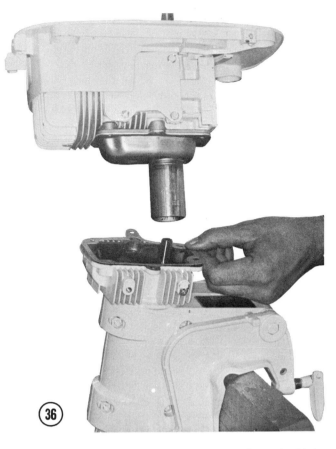

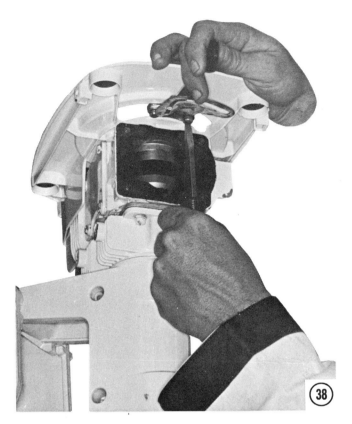

③⑦ Install the stator plate, and then tighten the high-tension spark plug wire retaining bracket to the cylinder.

③⑧ Install the throttle lever.

③⑨ Install and tighten the friction adjustment screw so that the throttle lever can be advanced smoothly. The

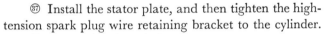

STATOR PLATE

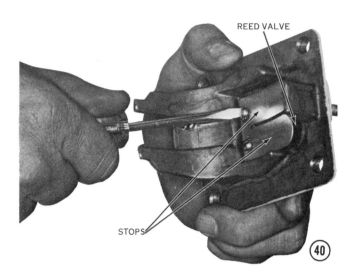

REED VALVE

STOPS

(40)

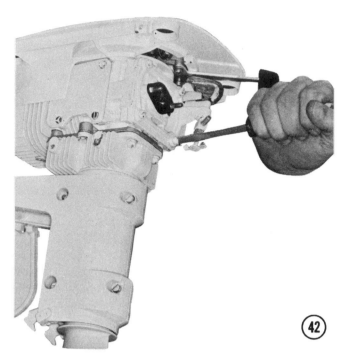

(42)

screw must be tight enough so that the stator plate will not creep from vibration. *NOTE: This adjustment should be made with the throttle lever in a central position.* A groove is provided in the cover plate for the purpose of reaching the screw.

⑩ Install new reed valves and reed-valve stops on the intake manifold casting. *CAUTION: The reed valves must lie flat against the reed-valve plate. If the reed valves or stops are bent or distorted, they must be replaced.*

⑪ To check the reed-valve stops, measure the distance from the surface to each stop, at its outer edge. This distance should measure 0.250"–0.280". *CAUTION: Don't attempt to adjust the stops by bending them; install new parts.*

⑫ Install the intake manifold, using a new gasket between the manifold and the crankcase.

⑬ Replace the carburetor, using a new gasket under the flange.

⑭ Position the cam over the crankshaft, making

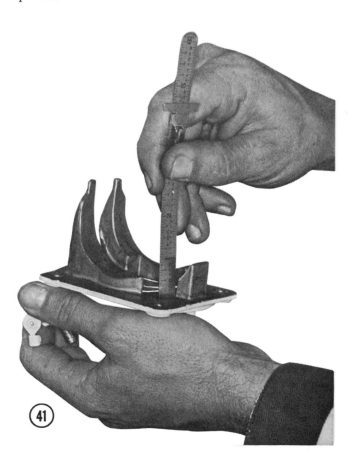

(41)

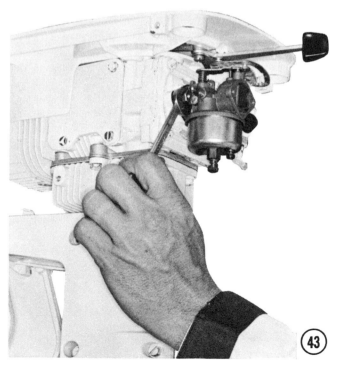

(43)

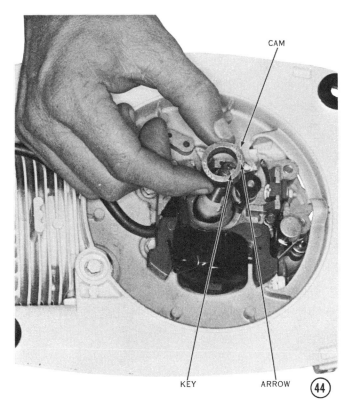

CAM

KEY   ARROW   (44)

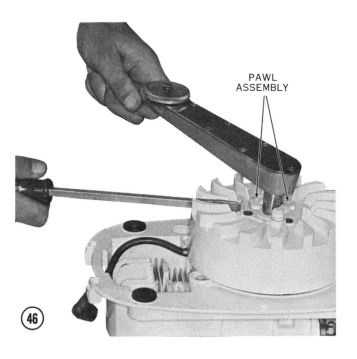

PAWL
ASSEMBLY

(46)

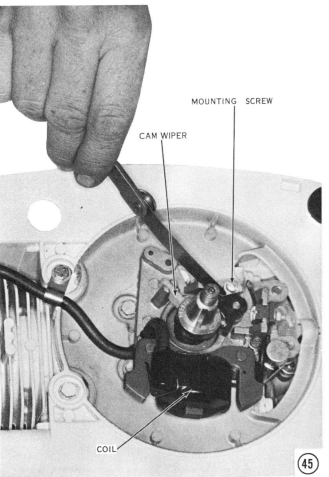

MOUNTING SCREW

CAM WIPER

COIL   (45)

sure that the direction-of-rotation arrow faces up as shown.

㊺ Install new breaker points. *CAUTION: Don't attempt to file old points; the result seldom is satisfactory.* When installing a new set of breaker points, clean the assembly thoroughly in carbon tetrachloride to remove the wax which protects the new points. This can be done by sloshing the parts around in a can of the cleaning solution. *CAUTION: Carbon tetrachloride is toxic. Make sure that the room is well ventilated. Avoid inhaling the fumes. Keep containers well capped when not in use.* After installing the breaker points, check for alignment. Misalignment will be in a side-to-side direction, if it exists; it can be corrected by forcing the stationary point in the proper direction. To adjust the point gap, rotate the crankshaft until the breaker arm rests on the high point of the breaker cam. Loosen the breaker point mounting screw, and then adjust the gap to 0.020″. *CAUTION: Clean the feeler gauge blade to avoid contaminating the breaker points with oil, which is an insulator.* Tighten the breaker point mounting screw, and then recheck the gap. Apply a few drops of light oil to the cam wiper. *CAUTION: Don't use too much oil, or some will get onto the points and cause trouble.*

㊻ Place the flywheel on the crankshaft and carefully push it down as far as it will go. Move the pawl assemblies out of the way, install the washer and nut, and then tighten it to 300–360 in.-lbs. of torque.

㊼ Replace the spark plug with a new Champion J14Y, with the gap adjusted to 0.035″. *CAUTION: Use a round gap gauge; a flat gauge will give a false reading.* Bend the ground electrode to make the adjustment.

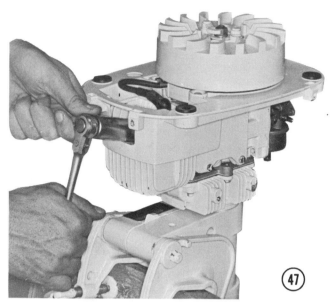

(47)

CAUTION: Don't bend the center electrode or you will crack the porcelain. Always replace the spark plug gasket; it is very important in providing the correct heat path for efficient cooling. Tighten the spark plug to 20 ft-lbs. of torque. *CAUTION: Support the rear of the spark plug socket to keep it from tilting, which would crack the porcelain.* Connect the high-tension wire to the spark plug terminal.

⑱ To replace the fuel tank, attach the fuel line, and

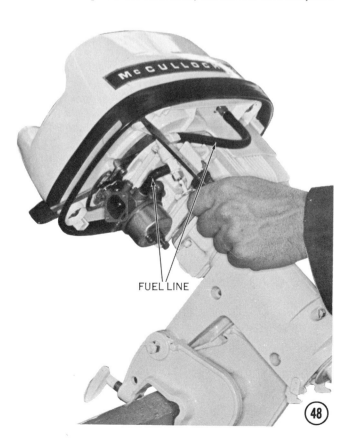

FUEL LINE

(48)

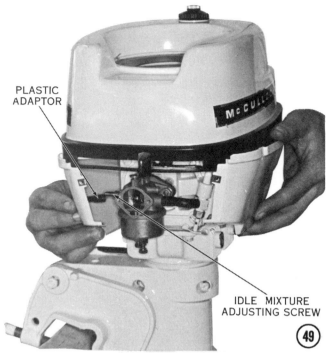

PLASTIC ADAPTOR

IDLE MIXTURE ADJUSTING SCREW

(49)

then install and tighten the four mounting screws from the underside of the cover plate.

⑲ Replace the skirt, making sure that the plastic adaptor fits over the carburetor idle mixture adjusting screw. Tighten the four retaining screws securely.

⑳ If the starter spring is broken, or if the unit has been taken apart, start the assembly with the rewind spring. If a new spring is to be installed, unfasten the

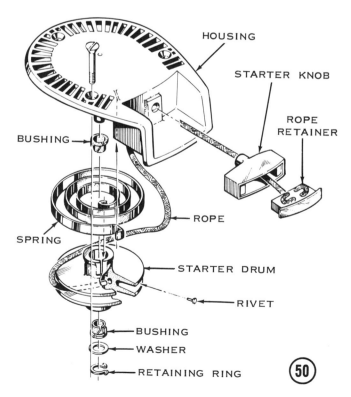

HOUSING

STARTER KNOB

ROPE RETAINER

BUSHING

ROPE

SPRING

STARTER DRUM

RIVET

BUSHING

WASHER

RETAINING RING

(50)

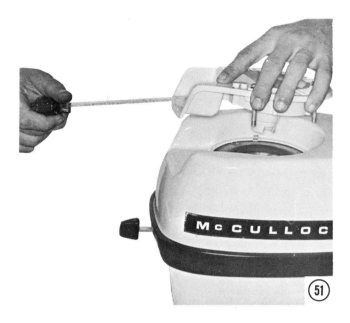

two clips which keep the spring tightly coiled. *CAU-TION: Release the spring carefully to avoid injury.* Cover the spring with a light coating of oil. Put the loop end of the spring into the slot provided on the rim of the housing. With the housing on the bench, upside down, wind the spring into the housing in a counterclockwise direction. *NOTE: The spring ends are softened to assist in making the spring conform to the shape of the drum and housing at the anchor ends.* Install one of the bushings in the housing. Thread the rope through the hole in the drum, and then install the rivet about 1/2″ from the end. Hold a lighted match under the end of the new rope to heat-seal the fibers and to keep it from unraveling. Dip the rope and rivet into sealer, and then allow it to dry. Pull back on the rope so that the rivet butts against the rope keeper. Make sure that the rivet head faces toward the outer rim of the starter drum. *CAUTION: If the other end of the rivet faces out, it will have a tendency to cut the rope.* With the drum upside down, wrap the rope in a counterclockwise direction and feed the end through the housing. Put the starting knob on the end of the rope, and then install the rope retainer. Slip the drum onto the shaft, engaging the spring in the slot. The bushing has a pip on its side and the inside of the shaft has a matching groove. *CAU-TION: The pip on the bushing must be lined up with the groove on the shaft, or the drum will not slide all the way into the housing.* Install the other bushing. Make sure to line up the pip on the housing with the groove on the shaft. Install and secure the washer with the retaining ring. Pull the starter knob until the rope is out of the housing about a foot, and then feed a little slack back through the slot in the housing. Hold the free end of the rope securely with one hand, and then wind the

starter drum with the rope in a counterclockwise direction (with the assembly upside down on the bench). This is to place tension on the spring; the slot in the drum allows the drum to rotate without taking in or letting out any of the rope. Increase tension on the spring until you feel the spring will hold the knob firmly against the housing. *NOTE: If you have about a foot of rope out of the housing, one turn probably will be enough. If you have more than a foot, it will take more than one turn.* Check the tension on the spring by pulling the rope out as far as it will go. Hold the rope knob out with one hand and, with the other, see if you can rotate the drum counterclockwise from three-quarters of a turn to a full turn. This check is necessary to make sure that the spring is not wound too tightly. *CAUTION: Winding the spring too tightly will result in unnecessary strain on the spring hooks when the rope is at its fully extended position.* After the starter is completely assembled, pull the rope out several times, and then allow it to return slowly to make sure that it operates freely and without binding. *CAUTION: Never release the rope from the extended position. The shock of the knob hitting the housing may damage both parts.*

㊿ To install the starter assembly on the early models with the retainers on the ring, first make sure that the retaining ring and the retainers are in place in the fuel tank opening. Install the two retainers on the starter ring at the grooves provided for this purpose, and then snap the ring onto the fuel tank. Pull the rope all the way out, and then let it return slowly while you ease the starter assembly into position. The rotation of the shaft, as the

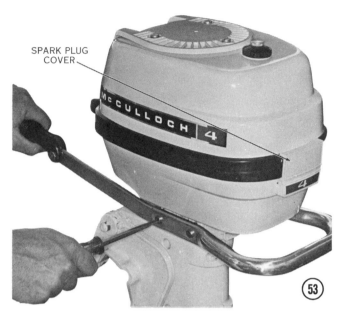

SPARK PLUG COVER

(53)

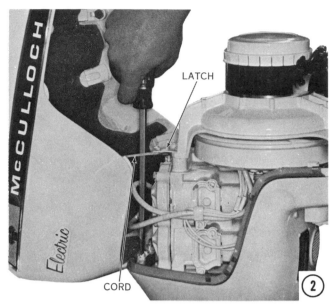

LATCH

CORD

(2)

starter rewinds, will throw the flywheel pawls out, and this will allow the starter assembly to drop into place. Tighten the mounting screws to 25 in.-lbs. of torque.

㉒ Replace the front panel by pushing in on the choke knob while leading the rod into the choke lever. Bend the rod lock to keep the rod from dropping out of the choke lever. Replace the four retaining screws, tightening them securely.

㉓ Replace the spark plug cover and retain it with the two screws. Replace the steering handle, tightening the four capscrews securely.

DISASSEMBLING

① Release the hood by lifting both side latches all the way.

② Remove the two screws holding the hood at the rear hinge, detach the cord from its latch, and then remove the hood assembly.

③ Disconnect the high-tension leads from the spark plugs. Take out the spark plugs, using a 13/16″ deep socket. *CAUTION: Support the rear of the spark plug*

OVERHAULING A TWO-CYLINDER, 7.5 AND 9 HP ENGINE

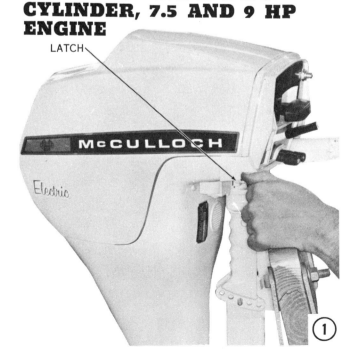

LATCH

(1)

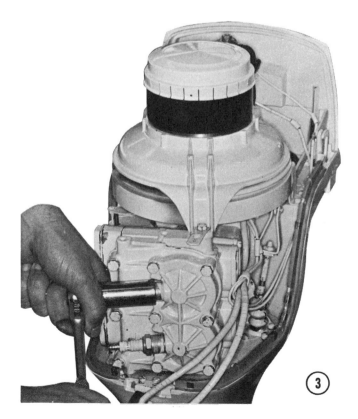

(3)

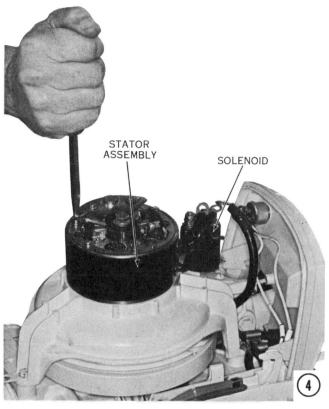

STATOR ASSEMBLY

SOLENOID

④

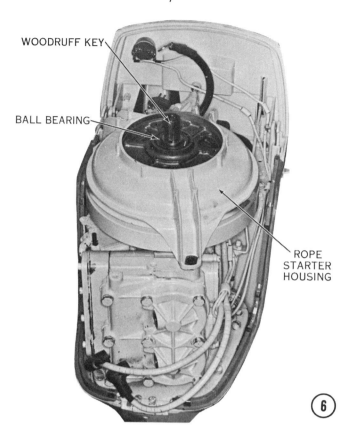

WOODRUFF KEY

BALL BEARING

ROPE STARTER HOUSING

⑥

socket to keep it from tilting, which would crack the porcelain.

④ Lift the cap off the starter-generator. Disconnect the wires that lead to the solenoid. Remove the through-bolts, and then lift off the stator assembly.

⑤ Pull out the starter rope, and then insert a retaining pin to hold the rope against the tension of the coil spring. Take out the bolt holding the armature to the crankshaft, and then lift off the armature.

⑥ Take out the three bolts holding the starter housing to the powerhead. Note the position of the rope latch on the rear bolt so that it can be replaced properly. Pry out the Woodruff key, and then lift off the starter housing. Remove the ball bearing from the starter housing.

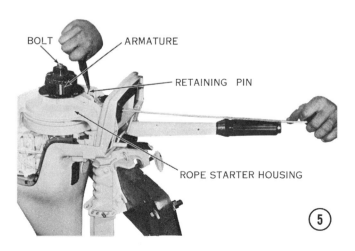

BOLT

ARMATURE

RETAINING PIN

ROPE STARTER HOUSING

⑤

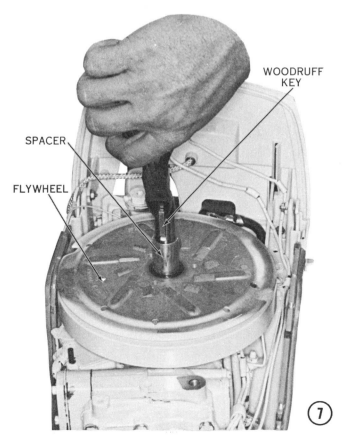

WOODRUFF KEY

SPACER

FLYWHEEL

⑦

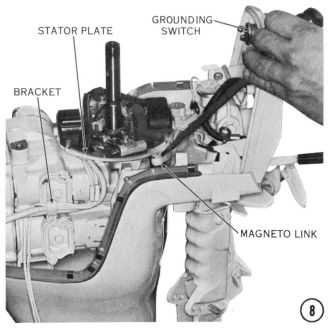

STATOR PLATE

GROUNDING SWITCH

BRACKET

MAGNETO LINK

⑧

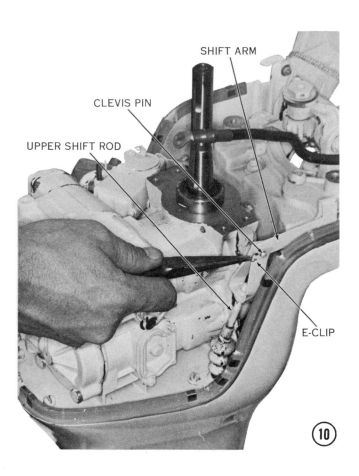

SHIFT ARM

CLEVIS PIN

UPPER SHIFT ROD

E-CLIP

⑩

⑦ Lift out the long spacer. Lift the flywheel straight up to remove it. Pry out the Woodruff key.

⑧ Remove the breaker cam from the crankshaft. Disconnect the primary wires from the ignition grounding switch. Pry the magneto link from the pin on the stator plate. Disconnect the wiring harness by taking out the wiring harness bracket retaining screw.

⑨ Rotate the stator plate until the holes are over the bolt heads so that you can remove the bolts which retain the hold-down clamps. Remove both hold-down clamps and the friction springs under them. Lift off the

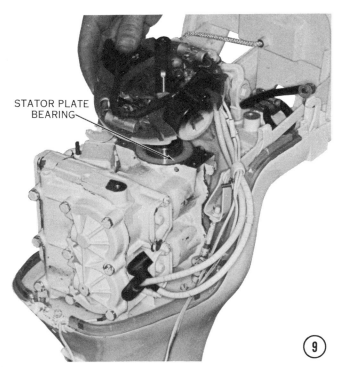

STATOR PLATE BEARING

⑨

⑪

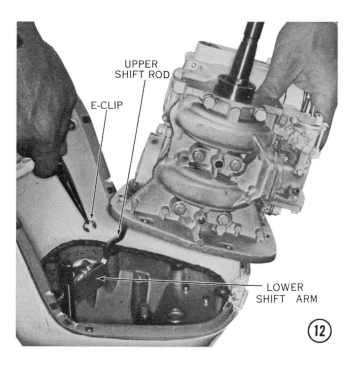

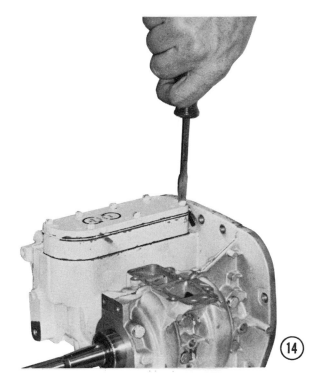

stator plate assembly, and then take off the stator plate bearing which is located between the stator plate and the powerhead.

⑩ Disconnect the shift arm from the upper shift rod by removing the E-clip and the clevis pin.

⑪ Disconnect the fuel line to the carburetor inlet. Remove the powerhead retaining screws.

⑫ Lift the powerhead up as far as possible, and then remove the E-clip holding the upper shift rod to the lower shift arm.

⑬ Take out the two screws holding the upper shift rod retainer to the crankcase flange. Remove the overflow line from the carburetor to the fitting on the crankcase flange. Take out the four retaining screws, and then lift off the carburetor and the reed-valve plate assembly under it. *CAUTION: Handle the reed-valve assembly with care to avoid damaging the reed valves.*

⑭ Remove the exhaust manifold, cover plates, and all gaskets.

⑮ Take off the cylinder head and the gasket.

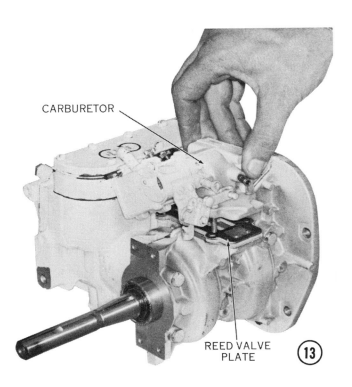

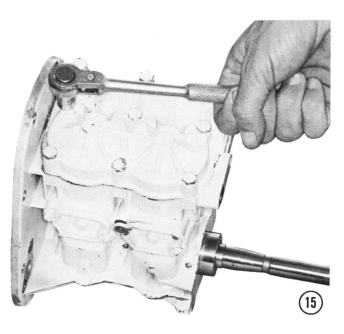

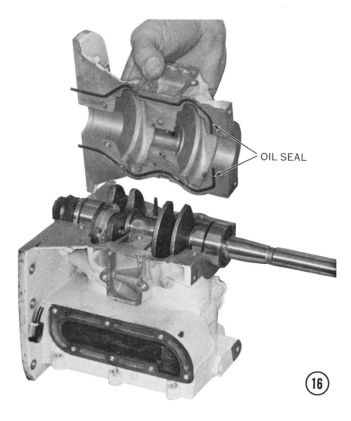

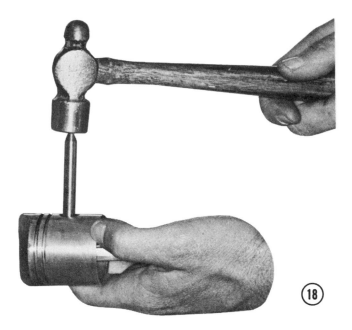

⑯ Take out the six bolts holding the crankcase to the cylinder assembly, and then lift off the crankcase. Remove the oil seal.

⑰ Remove the cap bolts. Position each cap as shown to avoid mixing them. Take out the roller bearings, and then lift out the crankshaft assembly. Replace the rod caps on their respective connecting rods, match-

ing up the alignment dots. Pull out each piston and rod assembly.

⑱ Remove the piston rings. Take out the piston pin locks, and then drive the piston pin from the piston and rod. *CAUTION: Support the rod to keep from bending it.*

CLEANING AND INSPECTING

Examine the crankcase-cylinder assembly carefully for cracks and damaged gasket surfaces, both inside and out. Check the bearing bore for scoring, gouging, wear, and out-of-round. Replace the crankcase assembly if the bores show evidence of bearing seizure or galling. Light or moderate scoring of the bronze center main bearing

This picture shows the scuffing caused by an improper fuel and oil mixture. It pays to be careful in mixing the oil and gasoline.

will have no significant effect on the operation of the engine.

Examine the cylinder bores for scores. If cracks or severe scoring is found, the crankcase-cylinder assembly must be replaced. Replacement, of course, also requires new pistons and rings. A moderately scored cylinder can be rebored 0.020″ oversize. Oversize pistons and rings are available for service. Always check each cylinder bore for an out-of-round condition. Use a dial indicator to determine the amount of cylinder bore wear. Take readings at different points around the cylinder bore to indicate the degree of out-of-round.

Taper is found by positioning the dial indicator at the top and then at the bottom of the ring-travel area. The difference between the top and bottom readings is the amount of taper in the cylinder bore.

Taper also can be measured with a new piston ring, if a dial indicator is not available. To use a piston ring for this purpose, place it in the cylinder bore; use a piston to square it with the cylinder bore. Measure the ring end gap at the bottom of the cylinder and record the measurement. Now push the ring to the top of the

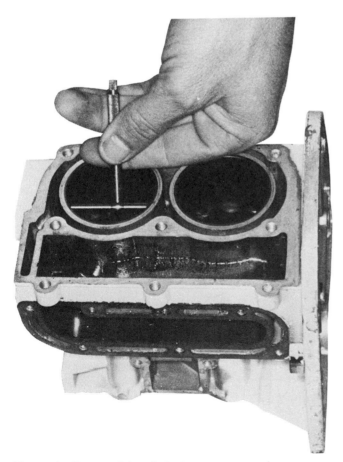

Measure the diameter of the cylinder bore at several places to determine the amount of wear and taper.

cylinder, again using the piston to keep the ring square, and then measure the end gap in the new position. The gap at the top of the cylinder will be greater because of the taper, and the difference between the reading at the top and bottom of the cylinder is the amount of taper.

If the taper or out-of-round measurement exceeds 0.005″, the cylinder should be rebored and honed and oversize pistons and rings installed. Reboring and honing also can be used to clear up cases of scoring, if the scores are not too deep.

Always measure a rebored cylinder and the diameter of the oversize piston to be installed. Measure the piston just below the lower ring groove. The correct sidewall clearance should be 0.0025″–0.0035″.

After a cylinder has been rebored or honed, it must be cleaned thoroughly. Swab the inside of the cylinder with a rag soaked in SAE 10 oil, and then wipe it out with a clean, dry cloth. Repeat the swabbing and wiping several times until a clean cloth shows no dirt or discoloration. *CAUTION: Don't use gasoline or solvent to clean the cylinder bore because these liquids cannot remove the abrasive which is left on the cylinder walls after honing.* If allowed to remain, the abrasives will cause very rapid wear on the cylinder walls and on the pistons and rings, and this will result in a greatly shortened engine life.

Proper cleaning of the cylinder walls is exceedingly important. Use a wire brush or a wooden scraper to remove the carbon deposits in and around the exhaust ports. Clean the ports with a cloth soaked in SAE 10 oil, and then wipe the surface dry with a clean cloth. Clean the cylinder bores in the same way.

Piston and Piston Pin

Examine the piston carefully for a scuffed or scored skirt or cracked or distorted ring lands. Discard the piston if any such defect is found. To clean the piston, soak it in solvent to loosen the carbon in the ring grooves. Remove the carbon with a ring groove scraper, which can be made by breaking an old piston ring and filing one end square for a scraping edge. *CAUTION: Be careful not to nick the ring groove side walls, as these are sealing surfaces. CAUTION: Never buff the piston with a wire brush.* Rinse the piston in solvent and wipe it clean with a dry cloth.

Examine the piston pin for wear and replace it if any wear is noted. Always replace the pin if a new piston is to be installed.

Piston Rings

Always replace the piston rings whenever the engine is disassembled for service. Even though the rings appear to be in good condition, they have been subjected to wear, pressure, and constant tension. In addition, they

Use the broken end of a piston ring to scrape the carbon from the ring grooves. CAUTION: Be careful not to nick the sides of the ring grooves, which are the sealing surfaces for the new rings.

can take a permanent set if the engine has been severely overheated.

To fit a new set of piston rings, push the new ring down into the bore of the cylinder with an inverted piston to make sure that the ring is square with the

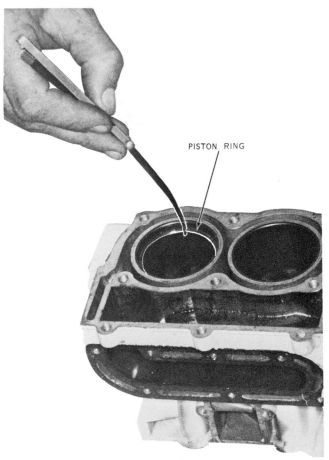

To measure the piston ring end gap, push a new piston ring into the cylinder bore, square it up with an inverted piston, and then measure the gap with a feeler gauge.

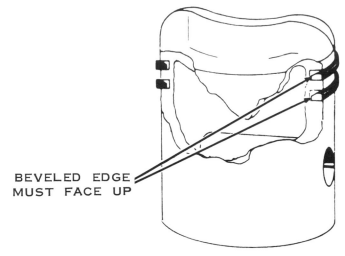

BEVELED EDGE MUST FACE UP

When installing new piston rings, make sure that the inner beveled edges of the rings face up.

cylinder bore. The ring should be positioned just above the exhaust ports. Measure the ring end gap, which should be 0.008″–0.012″. If the end gap is less than 0.008″, file the ends until the correct gap is obtained. Repeat the process with the second ring. *CAUTION: If the end gap is less than 0.008″, expansion will cause the ends to butt together, causing cylinder wall scuffing and possible seizure.*

To check the side clearance of the piston rings in the grooves of the piston, place a new ring in each groove. Rotate the rings around the grooves to make sure that they are free. Use a feeler gauge to check the side clearance between the rings and the grooves, which should be 0.0015″–0.0040″. If the clearance is more or less than specifications, replace the piston.

Two-cycle engine piston rings are especially designed for this type of service. Some of them have low outward

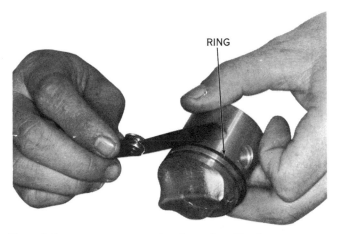

Use a feeler gauge to measure the piston ring side clearance.

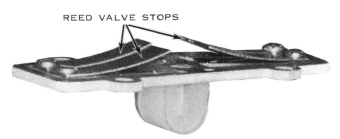

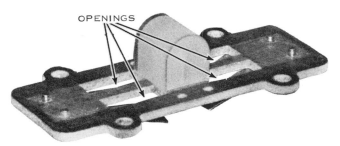

The reed-valve stops should be 1/4″ above the reed valves. CAUTION: The reed valves must cover the openings in the block perfectly.

This inverted reed-valve block shows the openings that can be seen when the reed valves are not properly centered over the openings in the block.

pressure at the ring ends so that there can be no tendency for the ends to hang up in the cylinder ports. *CAUTION: Using an improperly designed ring will result in piston ring breakage and cylinder wall scoring.*

Connecting Rod

Clean and examine the connecting rod for damage and wear. Look for scores on the bearing surfaces and twisting or bending of the rod.

Crankshaft

Examine the crankshaft bearing surfaces for scoring and galling. Look for a worn keyway, a sheared key, or stripped threads. Any burrs should be dressed down carefully with a fine file and then polished with crocus cloth. If the crankshaft is worn or damaged, it should be replaced. *CAUTION: It is more economical to replace a damaged crankshaft than it is to repair it. A poor repair job may result in damage to other parts of the engine, which always results in a greater expense than a new crankshaft.*

Bearings

Inspect ball bearings for abnormal wear and flat spots. Wash the bearing in gasoline or solvent and revolve it by hand to test for roughness. *CAUTION: Never spin a ball bearing with compressed air or you will damage the races.* After washing, lubricate the bearing with clean oil.

Inspect needle bearings for wear and for burned or

flattened rollers. Discard any defective bearings. The 24 connecting rod needle bearings should be replaced as a set if any are damaged, worn, or burned.

Oil Seals

Examine the oil seals and gaskets thoroughly for cuts and wear. Always replace all oil seals because of the possibility of air leaks and a crankcase pressure loss.

Clean the crankcase cover thoroughly with solvent, removing all dirt and foreign material. Inspect the gasket surfaces for burrs, which might cause difficulty in sealing. Clean the crankcase cover gasket surfaces thoroughly. Examine the screw hole threads. If the threads are stripped, make a repair with a Heli-Coil insert.

Reed Valves

Inspect the reed-valve plate assembly for defects. The reed valves must lie flat against the reed plate and they must cover the openings fully. Any gap will result in leakage and poor engine performance.

ASSEMBLING

⑲ Press the piston pin into place. The sloping portion of the piston dome must face the exhaust port when installed in the cylinder. The oil hole in the connecting

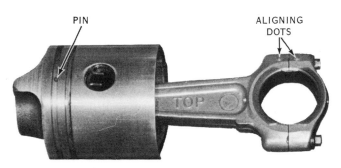

The alignment pin for the top ring groove must be on the same side as the aligning dots.

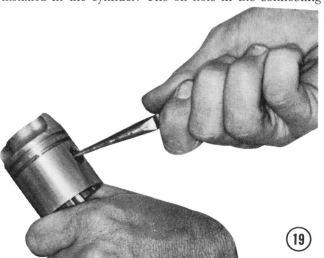

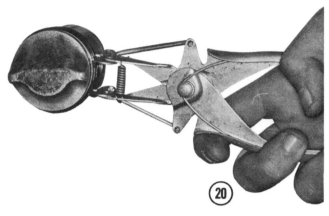

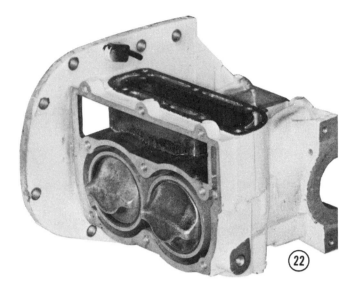

rod and the word TOP must face the flywheel end of the engine. Replace both piston pin locks.

㉚ Use a ring expander to install new piston rings. Using an expander tool keeps from giving the new piston rings a permanent set. *CAUTION: The beveled edge of each piston ring must face the top of the piston.*

HOLES

LOCATING DOWELS

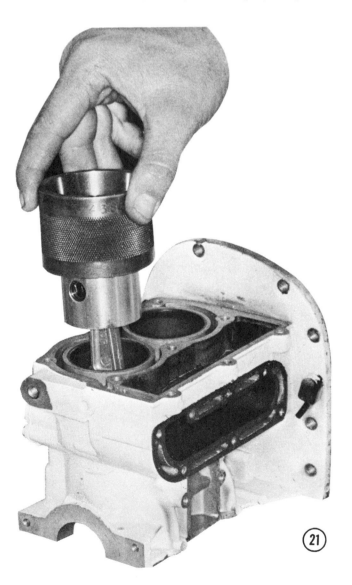

(25)

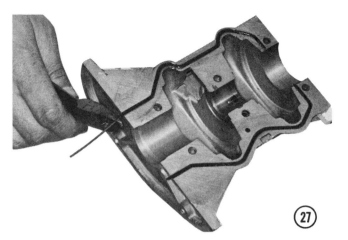

(27)

Line up the end gaps so that they are over the pins.

㉑ Oil the piston and rings, and then use a piston ring compressor to help in the installation. The tapered face of the illustrated compressor allows you to push the assembled piston through the compressor and into the cylinder bore without damaging or breaking a piston ring.

㉒ Turn the assembled block upside down to check that you have the pistons installed with the deflectors in the position shown.

㉓ Remove the connecting rod caps, and then position them as shown so that the parts will not be mixed. Lay the crankshaft into position, aligning the locating dowels with the matching holes in the bearing shells.

㉔ Snap in the steel bearing races. Grease the caps and rods so that the roller bearings will stay in place

during assembly. Install the roller bearings in the rod, and then pull the rod up into position around the crankshaft journal.

㉕ Grease the crankpin journal, and then fill it with the roller bearings. Replace each cap, matching the aligning dot with the dot on the connecting rod half.

㉖ Tighten the rod cap retaining bolts to 40–45 in.-lbs. torque.

㉗ Install new rubber oil seals in the grooves of the crankcase. Cut off the excess length, allowing about 1/4″ to extend past the edge of the casting. Apply a moderate layer of Permatex No. 3 along the outside edge of each rubber seal. *CAUTION: Don't apply too much sealer and don't apply it to the inside faces of the crankcase flanges, or the excess will be squeezed into the bearings and valves.*

㉘ Lay the crankcase on the block, aligning the dowel in the crankcase with the hole in the block. Bolt

(26)

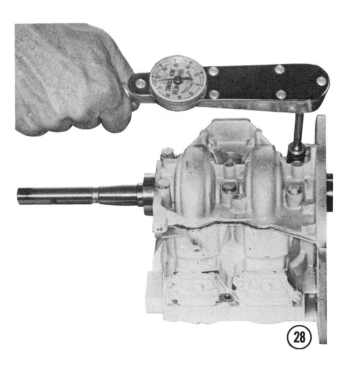

(28)

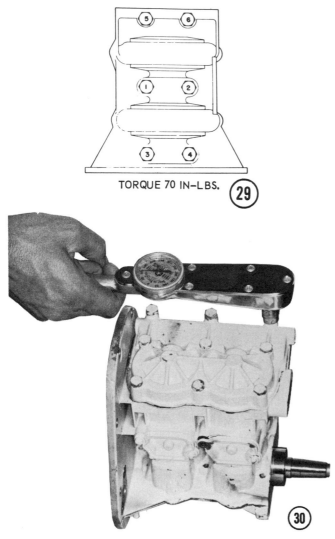

TORQUE 70 IN-LBS. (29)

TORQUE 100 IN-LBS (31)

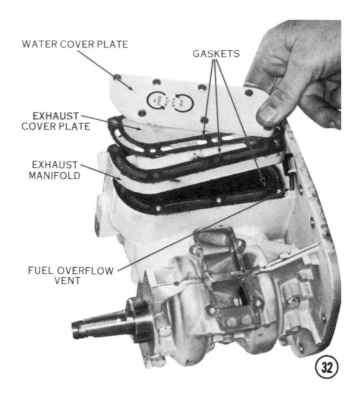

WATER COVER PLATE
GASKETS
EXHAUST COVER PLATE
EXHAUST MANIFOLD
FUEL OVERFLOW VENT

(32)

the crankcase to the block, torquing the bolts to 70 in.-lbs. in the sequence shown in the next illustration.

㉙ This drawing shows the correct sequence for torquing the crankcase bolts. *CAUTION: It is important to tighten the bolts in this order to avoid distorting the crankcase and cylinder bores.*

㉚ Apply a light coating of grease to both sides of the cylinder head gasket, and then install the cylinder

head, tightening the retaining bolts to 100 in.-lbs. of torque in the sequence shown in the next illustration.

㉛ This drawing shows the correct sequence for torquing the cylinder head bolts. *CAUTION: It is important to tighten the bolts in this order to avoid distorting the cylinder bores.*

㉜ Replace the exhaust manifold and cover plates in the order shown. Be sure to use a new gasket between each of the parts. Tighten the retaining screws evenly.

㉝ Install new reed valves and stops, tightening the retaining screws securely. *NOTE: The reeds are designed to lie flat against the reed plate. To assure a flat fit, the reeds have a slight bend near their mounting holes and they should be installed so that the spring loads them against the plates. CAUTION: Make sure that the reed valves cover the ports evenly.* Note how these top two reed valves are incorrectly positioned, leaving an opening which will cause operating difficulties.

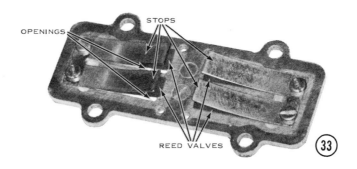

OPENINGS   STOPS

REED VALVES   (33)

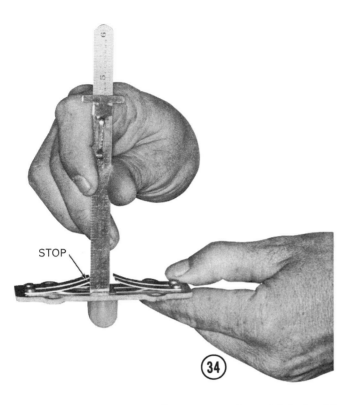

STOP

(34)

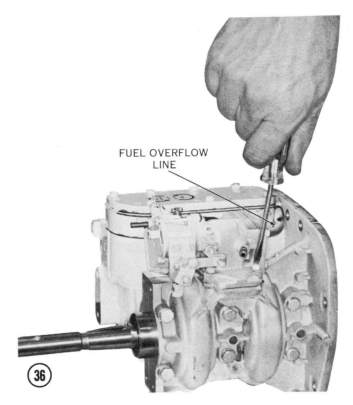

FUEL OVERFLOW
LINE

(36)

㉞ Check the reed valve stop opening, which should be 1/4", measured from the tip of the stop to the reed plate.

㉟ Install the assembled reed-valve plate, using a new gasket on each side of it.

㊱ Replace the carburetor over the reed-valve plate, and then tighten the four retaining screws evenly. *CAUTION: Make sure that a new gasket is positioned between the carburetor and the reed-valve plate assembly.* Attach the fuel overflow line from the float bowl to the fitting on the crankcase flange. On later models, the overflow hose is routed through a hole in the lower engine casing.

㊲ Install the upper shift rod, tightening the two retaining screws securely.

㊳ Place a new gasket in the lower engine casing, and then check the inside of the casing to be sure that

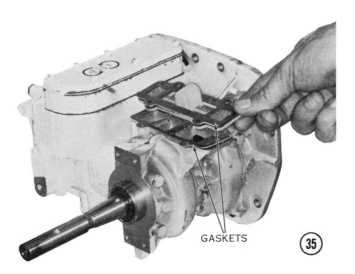

GASKETS   (35)

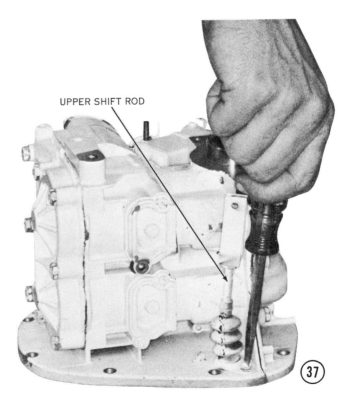

UPPER SHIFT ROD

(37)

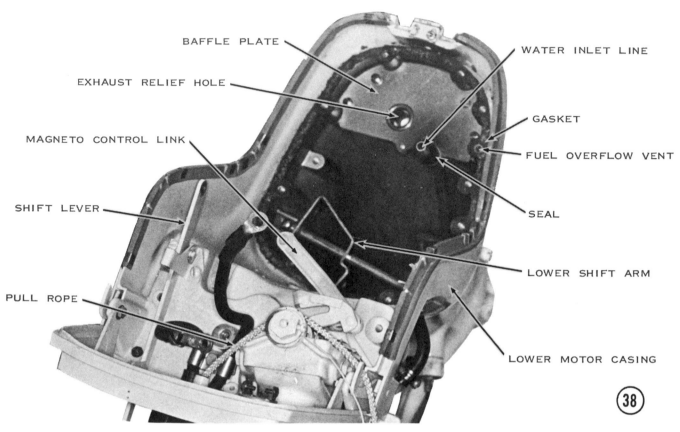

BAFFLE PLATE

EXHAUST RELIEF HOLE

MAGNETO CONTROL LINK

SHIFT LEVER

PULL ROPE

WATER INLET LINE

GASKET

FUEL OVERFLOW VENT

SEAL

LOWER SHIFT ARM

LOWER MOTOR CASING

(38)

all parts are in place ready to receive the assembled powerhead.

③⑨ Attach the upper shift rod to the lower shift arm with the clevis pin. Secure it with a new E-clip, and then lower the assembled powerhead into the lower engine casing.

④⓪ If the lower unit is already in position, it may be necessary to install a bolt in the crankshaft to turn it

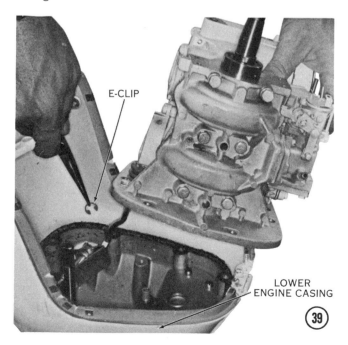

E-CLIP

LOWER
ENGINE CASING

(39)

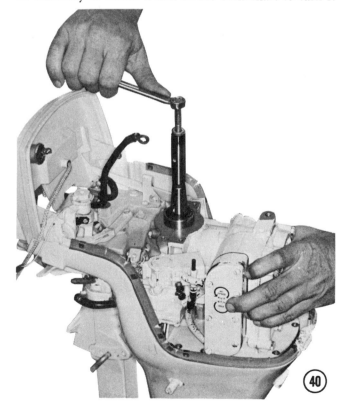

(40)

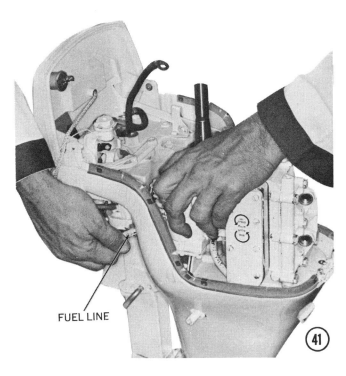

FUEL LINE

(41)

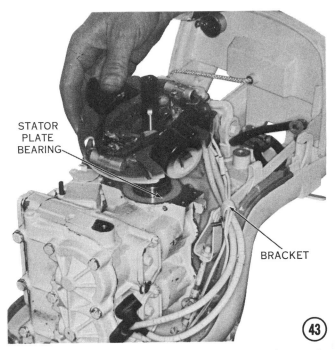

STATOR
PLATE
BEARING

BRACKET

(43)

in order to align the splines. Tighten the retaining screws securely.

④① Connect the fuel line to the carburetor inlet fitting. Make sure that the spring clamp holds the line securely.

④② Connect the upper shift rod to the shift arm with a clevis pin. Secure the linkage with a new E-clip.

④③ Position the stator plate bearing over the crankshaft, and then install the stator plate assembly. Secure the high-tension wire bracket to the crankcase.

④④ Install a hold-down clamp and a friction spring on each side of the stator plate. The ears of the clamps must fit into the grooves of the stator plate. Rotate the plate until the access holes are directly above the capscrews, and then tighten them securely.

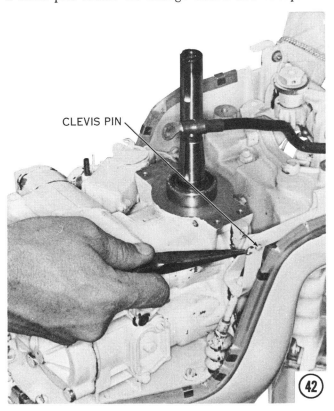

CLEVIS PIN

(42)

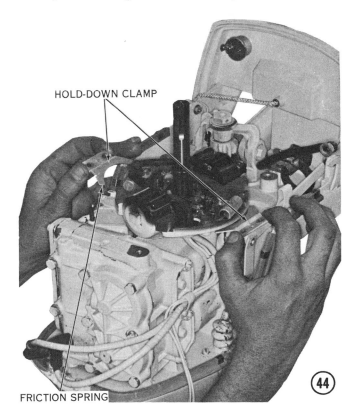

HOLD-DOWN CLAMP

FRICTION SPRING

(44)

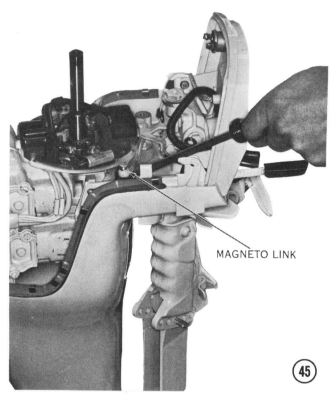

MAGNETO LINK

(45)

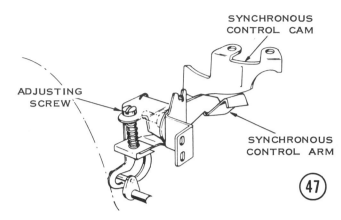

SYNCHRONOUS
CONTROL CAM

ADJUSTING
SCREW

SYNCHRONOUS
CONTROL ARM

(47)

④⑤ Force the socket of the magneto link over the pin of the stator plate.

④⑥ Synchronize the stator plate position with the

throttle by turning the twist-grip handle to the slow position. Slowly turn the twist-grip handle toward the fast position until the synchronous control arm touches the synchronous control cam at the alignment mark. Turn the adjusting screw, if necessary, until the control arm just contacts the cam at the alignment mark. Retard the throttle, and then recheck the adjustment.

④⑦ This drawing shows the position of the synchronous cam and control arm in greater detail.

④⑧ Install the breaker cam. Spread the breaker points to assist in assembly. Install new breaker points. *CAUTION: Don't attempt to file the old points; the result is*

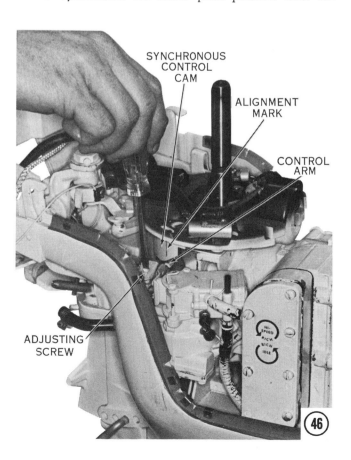

SYNCHRONOUS
CONTROL
CAM

ALIGNMENT
MARK

CONTROL
ARM

ADJUSTING
SCREW

(46)

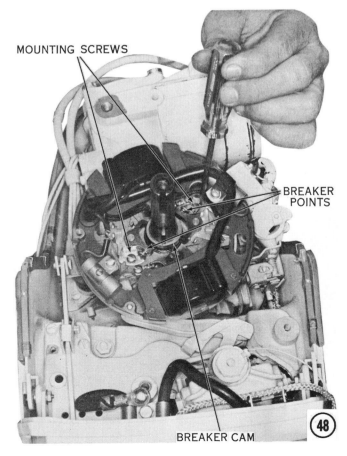

MOUNTING SCREWS

BREAKER
POINTS

BREAKER CAM

(48)

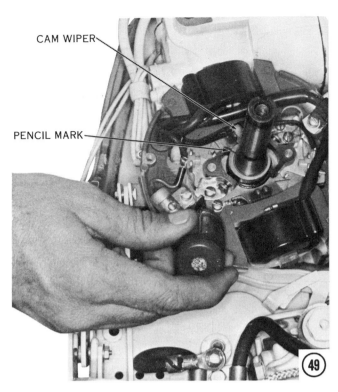

CAM WIPER

PENCIL MARK

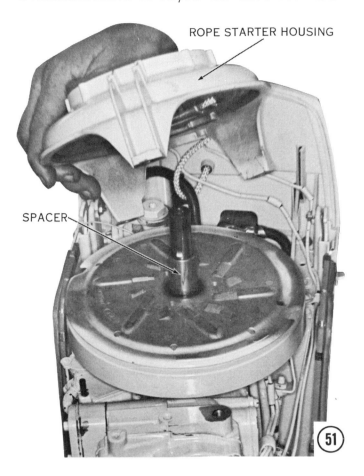

ROPE STARTER HOUSING

SPACER

seldom satisfactory. When installing new breaker points, clean the parts thoroughly in carbon tetrachloride to remove the wax which protects the new points. This can be done by sloshing the parts around in a can of the cleaning solution. *CAUTION: Carbon tetrachloride is toxic. Make sure that the room is well ventilated. Avoid*

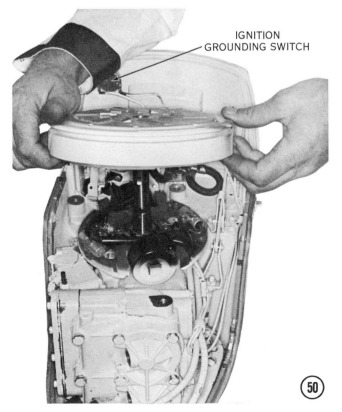

IGNITION GROUNDING SWITCH

inhaling the fumes. Keep the container well capped when not in use. After installing the breaker points, check for alignment. Misalignment will be in a side-to-side direction, if it exists; it can be corrected by forcing the stationary point in the proper direction. To adjust the point gap, rotate the crankshaft until the breaker arm rests on the high point of the breaker cam, and then adjust the gap of one set of points to 0.020″ by loosening the mounting screw and prying the stationary plate as required. *CAUTION: Measure the breaker point gap with a clean feeler gauge to avoid contaminating the breaker points with oil, which is an insulator.* Tighten the breaker point mounting screw, and then recheck the gap.

㊽ Make a pencil mark on the top surface of the high point of the cam, at the exact point where the breaker arm touches it. Turn the crankshaft exactly 180° until the pencil mark is against the breaker arm of the second set of breaker points, and then adjust the gap to 0.020″. Apply a few drops of light oil to the cam wiper. *CAUTION: Too much oil will get onto the points and cause trouble.*

㊾ Install the primary wires on the ignition grounding switch (stop button). Replace the Woodruff key in the keyway in the crankshaft. Install the flywheel.

㊿ Replace the rope starter assembly. If the starter has been disassembled, make sure that the eye in the

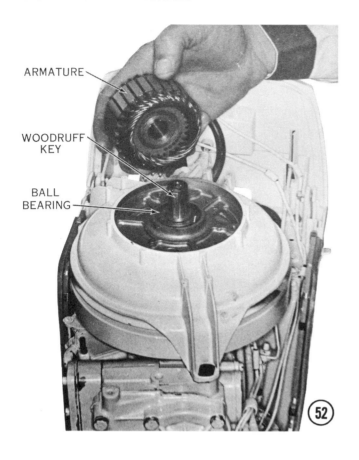

ARMATURE

WOODRUFF
KEY

BALL
BEARING

52

54

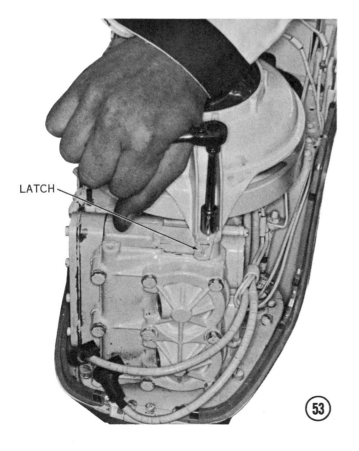

LATCH

53

recoil spring is seated on the pin in the starter housing. Wind the rope onto the pulley in a counterclockwise direction when looking at the pawl side of the pulley. Place the pulley in the starter housing, making sure that the inside end of the recoil spring is located on the pin or hook of the pulley hub. Wind the pulley one full turn counterclockwise, when looking at the pulley from the pawl side, thread the rope through the housing, and then knot it. Replace the long spacer, and then install the starter assembly. *CAUTION: Don't tighten the retaining bolts until the ball bearing has been installed.*

52 Install the ball bearing into the bore of the starter housing. Replace the Woodruff key in the keyway, and then install the starter-generator armature; tighten the retaining bolt securely.

53 Now tighten the three starter housing retaining bolts, making sure that the hood rope latch is positioned under the head of the bolt, as illustrated. *CAUTION: In order to establish the proper alignment, refrain from tightening the retaining bolts until the ball bearing is in place.* Any deviation in alignment may cause severe damage to the stator assembly fields and to the armature.

54 Replace the stator assembly. Pry the brushes apart to clear the commutator. Install and tighten the three through-bolts to 225 in.-lbs. torque.

55 Connect the wires to the starter solenoid, and then snap on the cap.

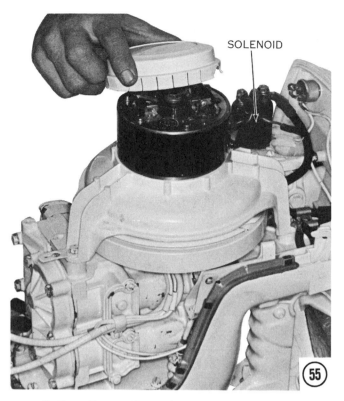

SOLENOID

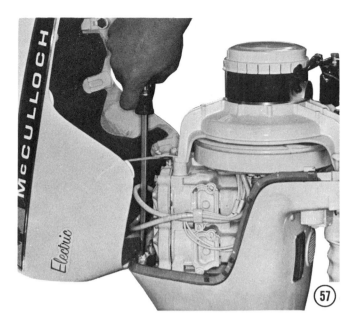

(55)

(57)

⑤ Install new Champion H10J spark plugs for the 7.5 Hp engine and AC CS45T spark plugs for the 9 Hp engine. Gap the spark plugs to 0.035". *CAUTION: Use a round gap gauge; a flat one will give a false reading. CAUTION: Bend the ground electrode to make the adjustment. If you bend the center electrode, you will crack the porcelain.* Always replace the spark plug gasket (except on the AC CS45T) as it is very important in

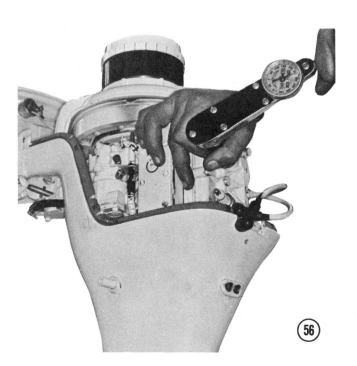

(56)

providing the correct heat path for efficient cooling. *NOTE: No gasket is used with the AC CS45T spark plug because it has a conical seat.* Tighten the spark plugs to 20 ft.-lbs. torque. *CAUTION: Support the rear of the spark plug socket to keep it from tilting, which would crack the porcelain.* Connect the high-tension wires to the spark plug terminals.

⑤ Attach the hood with the two retaining screws at the rear. Connect the restraining cord to the latch on the starter mount leg. Close the hood and snap it into position.

75, 45, 28, 14 & 3.5 ENGINE SERVICE NOTES

The powerheads of all these engines have many similarities with regard to the disassembly, inspection, and assembly of the components. This section will explain the procedures that differ from those discussed in the foregoing detailed sections on the 9, 7.5, and 4 Hp engines. The notes which follow cover the different service information that is needed to assemble them properly.

75 & 45 HP ENGINE SERVICE NOTES

The three-cylinder engine was rated at 60 Hp in 1960 and upgraded to 75 Hp in 1961. The largest of the two-cylinder engines was rated as 40 Hp in 1960, upgraded to 43 Hp in 1961, and upgraded again in 1963 to 45 Hp.

When the letter "B" appears at the end of the serial

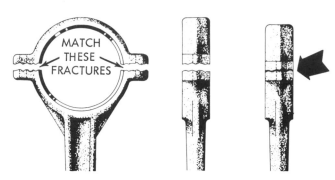

The steel rod caps are fractured, and this makes it imperative for the rod and cap to be carefully matched during assembly. When correctly assembled, the fraction lines should almost disappear. If assembled incorrectly and tightened, the parts will be ruined.

number, the cylinders are bored 0.030″ oversize. If the cylinder walls are damaged, they can be cleaned up with a finishing hone, removing 0.005″ stock. Corresponding oversize pistons and rings are available for service.

If the serial number does not end with the letter "B," then the cylinders can be bored to an oversize of 0.030″. Oversize pistons and rings are available for service.

The steel connecting rods are fractured, and this makes it imperative that the rod and cap are carefully matched during assembly. When correctly assembled, the fractured lines almost disappear. If the rod caps are assembled in reverse and then tightened, the fractured particles will break off, rendering the rod and cap useless. It is also important for the rods to be installed in the engine with the word TOP facing toward the flywheel end of the crankshaft.

When replacing the center main bearings, be sure to locate the bearing on the pin in the journal. On early models, the rollers are assembled in the slots around the outside of the bearing cage, one roller to each slot and one roller between the ends of the cage halves. Use grease to hold the bearing in place. The bearing races are fractured; be sure that the two halves are matched carefully. When assembling the bearings and cages, carefully match

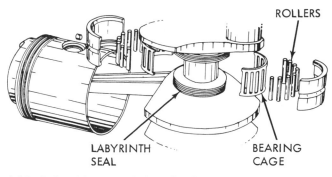

A labyrinth seal is composed of a series of grooves.

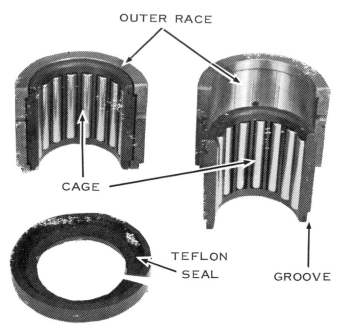

The main bearings were redesigned in 1962 to use a Teflon seal to replace the labyrinth seal of previous models.

the cage halves by mating the identifying ground corners.

Since 1964, a new style of center main bearing has been used. To remove this type of center main bearing from the crankshaft, remove the retaining ring. Slip the seal off the lower end of the bearing, and then remove it from the crankshaft. Separate the bearing races from the cages. Replacement bearings are sold as a set, which includes the bearing races, rollers, and cages. Seals are available separately.

To install the new style of main bearings, first make sure that the required number of rollers are installed in the slots in the bearing cages. Place the cage in the bearing race, and then locate it in the crankshaft journal so that the grooved end of the outer race is facing toward the lower end of the crankshaft. Place the outer cage in the outer race, and then locate these parts in the crankshaft journal so that the fractured edges of the outer race mate properly. Install the retaining ring in the groove cut into the outer race to secure the parts to the crankshaft.

The center main bearings were redesigned in 1965 to eliminate the cage between the rollers and the Teflon seal. The new bearing uses a labyrinth seal. To service the new main bearing, cover the rollers with grease to hold them in place. This bearing uses 26 rollers.

The center main bearing seal (labyrinth) is a groove cut into the crankshaft for some models. The labyrinth seals were replaced with Teflon seals on some models, starting in 1963. The main bearings have a groove on the lower end to accommodate the new type of seal.

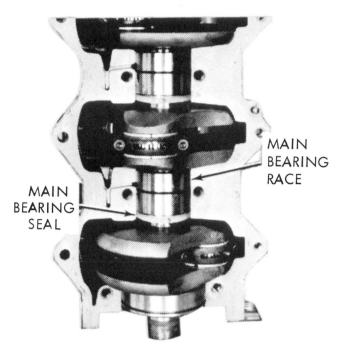

MAIN
BEARING
SEAL

MAIN
BEARING
RACE

This illustration shows how the Teflon seal is installed. The Teflon seal was used only during 1963—64 and was superseded in 1965 by the former labyrinth seal.

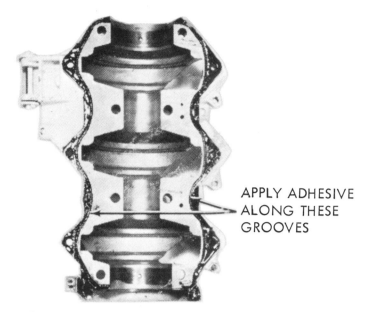

APPLY ADHESIVE
ALONG THESE
GROOVES

Before assembling the crankcase, apply adhesive along the grooves to seal the joint.

CAUTION: Make sure that the seals are installed before assembling the rest of the powerhead. Since 1965, a labyrinth seal has been used in place of the Teflon seal.

To install the Teflon seal, position it in the crankshaft journal so that it is seated over the groove cut into the lower end of the bearing race. Shift the cut ends so that they are not at the joint where the block and crankcase come together. As you install the crankshaft in the block, make sure that the outer race of the main bearing seats on the locating pin in the block.

Press the top and bottom main bearings on the crankshaft, using tool No. J-7657, until they bottom. NOTE: The lettering on the race should face out. The top and bottom crankshaft bearing seals are rubber on all models and should always be replaced.

Install the piston pin bearings with a special tool (No. J-7654) so that the lettering on the end of the bearing faces the outside of the piston. The bearing should be pressed in until the race is almost even with the boss on the inside of the piston.

A three-ring piston was used through 1963. Install the rings so that the inside beveled edges face the top of the piston. The rings should be installed so that the locating pin in the ring groove is centered in the open portion of each ring. Since 1964, a two-ring piston has been used. The new, thinner piston rings have a small beveled outside edge. CAUTION: Make sure to install the new rings with the side marked TOP facing the top of the piston. Install the piston in the block so that the sloping

portion of the piston dome faces the exhaust port side of the engine.

28 HP ENGINE SERVICE NOTES

The 28 Hp engine started as a 25 Hp unit. In 1961, it was upgraded to 27.7 Hp @ 4,800 rpm. In 1963, the speed was increased to 5,000 rpm and the engine was rated at 28 Hp.

To assemble the center main bearing on the crankshaft, use the same race, bearing cage, and bearings. Use grease to hold the bearings in place. Match the fractured halves of the bearing race and carefully replace the wire retainer.

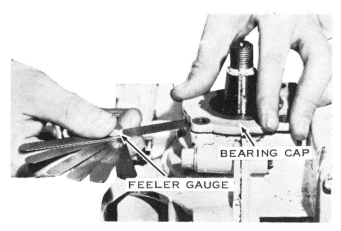

BEARING CAP

FEELER GAUGE

The end play of the crankshaft of the 75 Hp engine should be 0.010″ ± 0.002″. The end play of the 45 Hp engine crankshaft should be 0.000″ ± 0.002″. Shims are available for service.

Locate the crankshaft bearings on the pins in their respective journals, and then slide the graphite seal in place, followed by the rubber O-ring seal, washer, and spring lock. Secure the assembly by sliding the retaining ring on the crankshaft until it catches in the groove of the crankshaft.

Press the wrist pin bearings into the piston until the

edge of the bearing is even with the boss on the inside of the piston. When installing the bearings, press only against the lettered or stamped surface. *CAUTION: Support the piston to prevent distortion.*

With the piston and connecting rod installed in the engine, the sloping portion of the piston dome must face toward the exhaust port in the block. The oil hole in the

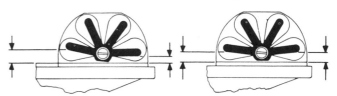

The reed valves used on the 28 Hp engine must be installed so that the reeds cover the openings fully, as shown on the right side of this picture.

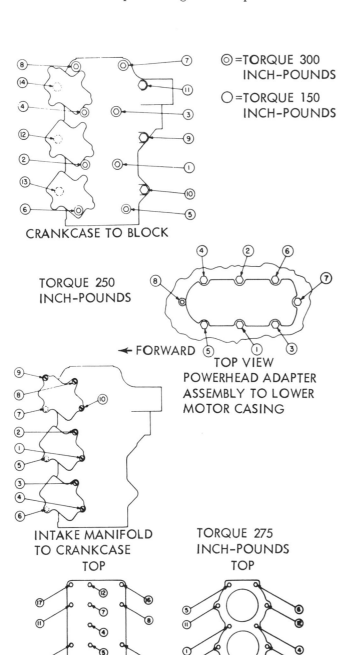

=TORQUE 300 INCH-POUNDS

=TORQUE 150 INCH-POUNDS

CRANKCASE TO BLOCK

TORQUE 250 INCH-POUNDS

← FORWARD

TOP VIEW POWERHEAD ADAPTER ASSEMBLY TO LOWER MOTOR CASING

INTAKE MANIFOLD TO CRANKCASE TOP

TORQUE 275 INCH-POUNDS TOP

EXHAUST COVER PLATE   CYLINDER HEAD

These diagrams show the proper sequence and the correct torque to use when tightening the various main castings of the 75 Hp engine.

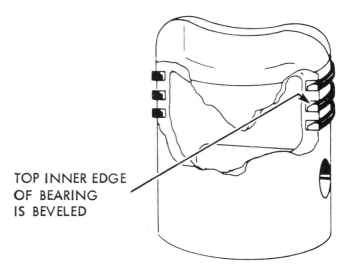

TOP INNER EDGE OF BEARING IS BEVELED

A three-ring piston was used on all engines through 1963. It was replaced by a two-ring piston in 1964.

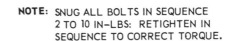

NOTE: SNUG ALL BOLTS IN SEQUENCE 2 TO 10 IN-LBS: RETIGHTEN IN SEQUENCE TO CORRECT TORQUE.

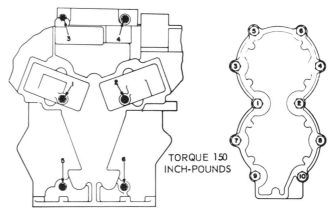

TORQUE 150 INCH-POUNDS

This diagram shows the proper sequence and the correct torque to use when tightening the various main castings of the 28 Hp engine.

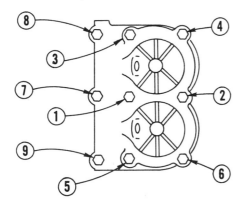

Use this sequence for tightening the cylinder head retaining bolts on the 7.5 and 9 Hp engines.

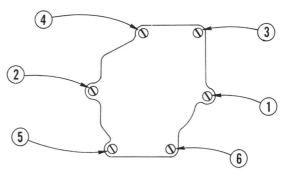

Use this sequence for tightening the muffler-to-block retaining bolts on the 7.5 and 9 Hp engines.

connecting rod must face the top of the engine.

The connecting rods are fractured. Be careful to match the fractured surfaces of the rod caps to the rods, and then torque the cap screws to 180 in.-lbs.

14 HP ENGINE SERVICE NOTES

The 14 Hp engine started out as a 12 Hp power-plant and was upgraded to 14 Hp in 1961. In 1964, a 140 OX model was introduced. This is the same 14 Hp engine added to a much heavier lower unit with a two-to-one gear reduction. Its designed purpose is to propel heavier craft: houseboats, rafts, and barges.

When installing a wrist pin, position the rod so that the side marked TOP faces toward the top of the engine. Heat the piston to 300°F. and chill the wrist pin before pressing it into the piston. The connecting rod should

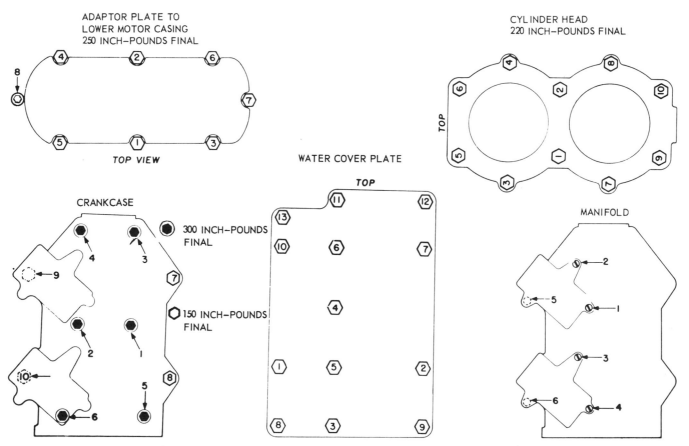

These diagrams show the proper sequence and the correct torque to use when tightening the various main castings of the 45 Hp engine.

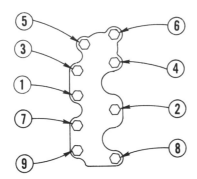

Use this sequence for tightening the cylinder head cover plate retaining bolts on the 7.5 and 9 Hp engines.

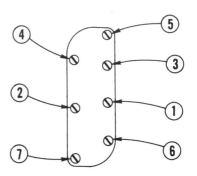

Use this sequence for tightening the exhaust cover plate retaining bolts on the 7.5 and 9 Hp engines.

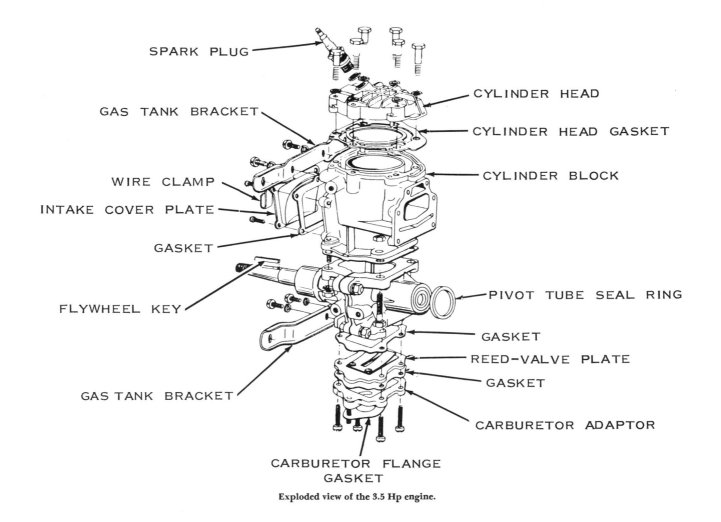

SPARK PLUG

GAS TANK BRACKET

WIRE CLAMP

INTAKE COVER PLATE

GASKET

FLYWHEEL KEY

GAS TANK BRACKET

CARBURETOR FLANGE GASKET

CYLINDER HEAD

CYLINDER HEAD GASKET

CYLINDER BLOCK

PIVOT TUBE SEAL RING

GASKET

REED-VALVE PLATE

GASKET

CARBURETOR ADAPTOR

Exploded view of the 3.5 Hp engine.

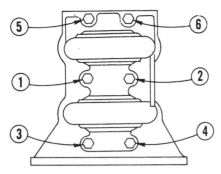

Use this sequence for tightening the crankcase retaining bolts on the 7.5 and 9 Hp engines.

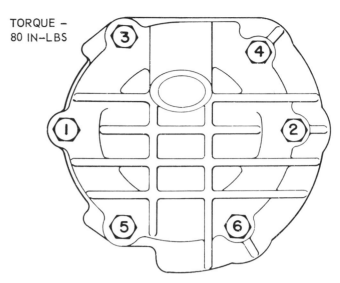

This diagram shows the proper sequence and the correct torque to use for tightening the cylinder head bolts on the 3.5 Hp engine.

be installed so that the side with the oil hole at the crank pin end of the rod faces toward the top of the engine.

The inside edge of each piston ring is beveled, and this side must face the dome of the piston. The rings should be installed so that the locating pin is centered in the open portion of each ring. Use a ring compressor to install the pistons. The sloping side of the piston must face toward the exhaust port side of the block.

3.5 ENGINE SERVICE NOTE

Heat the piston to 300°F. and chill the piston pin before installing it. The piston pin is secured in the piston with two piston pin locks, which must fit the grooves securely to prevent rapid enlargement of the grooves.

The piston rings should be installed so that the beveled inside edge of each ring faces the piston dome.

To fasten the connecting rod to the crankshaft, coat the rod and cap bearing surfaces with a layer of grease, and then lay 12 needle bearings in each half. Place the rod on the crankshaft with the piston baffle facing the flywheel end of the shaft. Place the cap in position over the rod so that the marks on the cap and rod are on the same side. Properly installed, the side of the rod marked TOP should face toward the flywheel.

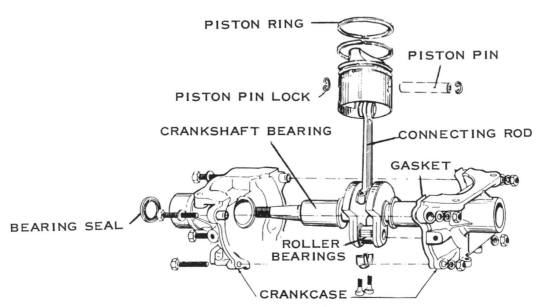

Details of the 3.5 Hp engine crankshaft and piston assembly.

6
SERVICING THE LOWER UNIT

DESCRIPTION

One-Cylinder Engine

The lower unit of the one-cylinder engine is a non-shift type, which also houses a water pump. Water enters the lower unit through a screen in the slotted front portion of the casing, from where it is pumped into the outlet cavity. When this space is filled, the impeller forces the water up through the water pipe, where it emerges to cool the lower engine casing. The powerhead is air cooled.

Two- and Three-Cylinder Engines

The lower unit contains the gears and shifting mechanism to provide a forward, neutral, and reverse range. In addition, water and bailer pumps are located

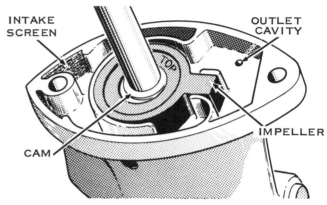

The eccentric cam causes the impeller to move in an eccentric motion, which forces the water into the lower engine casing of the 4 Hp unit.

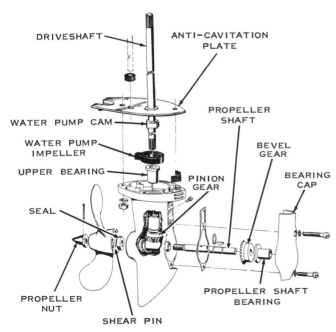

Exploded view of the lower unit of the 4 Hp engine.

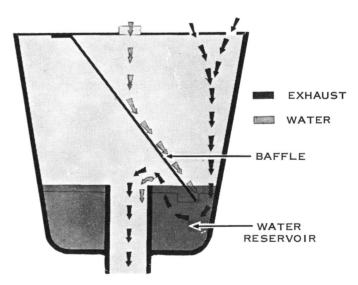

An idle-relief device is incorporated in all two-cylinder powerplants. The exhaust gases and the coolant from the powerhead are deflected downward into the idle-relief chamber by the baffle plate. Due to the height of the outlet tube, a constant level of water is maintained and the surplus is expelled through the outlet tube. Exhaust gases are forced to pass through the water before being expelled from the engine.

TOP VIEW

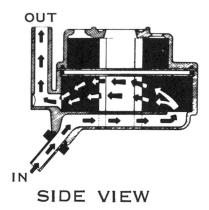

OUT

IN

SIDE VIEW

The water pump impellers on the larger units are positioned off center so that the rubber vanes bend and make the pumping chamber smaller or larger as the impeller turns.

at the top of the lower unit. Both pumps operate off the engine driveshaft, which turns the impellers in the pump bodies. Both pumps have separate water intake lines and discharge exits to prevent bilge water in the bailer system from being circulated through the engine cooling system.

The engine cooling water pump obtains its water supply from beneath the anti-cavitation plate and pumps the water up to the powerhead, where it is circulated around the exhaust cover plate, through the water jacket around the cylinders, and around the cylinder head. Then it is discharged into the idle relief chamber and into the lower engine casing.

The bailer pump draws bilge water from the bailer foot, and then discharges it into the lower engine casing, where it is carried away by the engine exhaust. Small bleed holes in the stainless steel plate, between the water pump and the bailer pump body, allow a small amount of water to bleed into the bailer pump to lubricate it when there is no bilge water.

SERVICE PROCEDURES

Service procedures for the lower unit of the one-cylinder engine will be discussed first, using step-by-step illustrated instructions. This will be followed by the service procedures for the two-cylinder unit, using the same techniques. The lower unit of the three-cylinder engine will be covered by exploded views.

ONE-CYLINDER ENGINE

DISASSEMBLY

① Remove the cotter key holding the propeller nut. Take off the nut, and then slide off the propeller.

② Take out the two screws, and then remove the bearing cap.

③ Remove the two nuts which hold the lower unit to the engine casing. Slide the lower unit, including the driveshaft and the anti-cavitation plate, down and away from the engine casing.

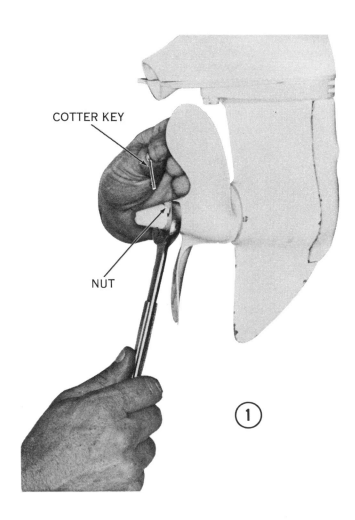

COTTER KEY

NUT

①

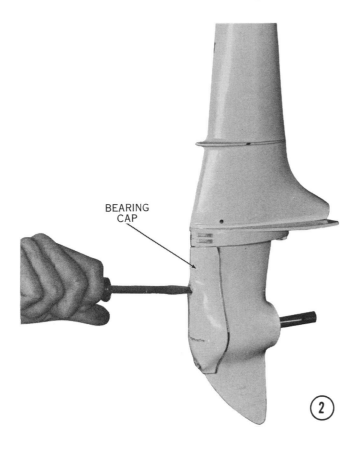

BEARING CAP

②

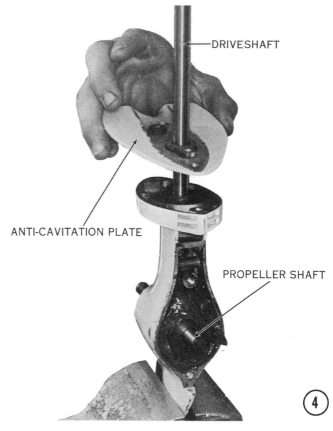

DRIVESHAFT

ANTI-CAVITATION PLATE

PROPELLER SHAFT

④

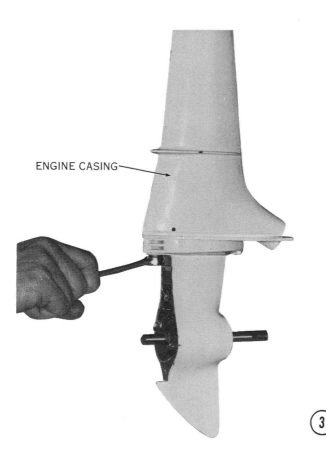

ENGINE CASING

③

④ Lift off the anti-cavitation plate. Dig the grease out with a wooden spatula. Pull out the propeller shaft. *NOTE: This releases the pinion gear from the driveshaft.* Remove the driveshaft. Lift the pinion gear out of the lower unit cavity. Remove the water pump impeller. *NOTE: The upper driveshaft bearing can be pulled out of the body, if necessary.*

CLEANING AND INSPECTING

Clean all parts in solvent and blow dry. A satisfactory inspection cannot be made with dirt masking the defects. After cleaning, inspect all parts for wear, rust, and other defects.

Seals
Always replace all seals and gaskets.

Water Pump
Check the water pump impeller for wear or broken vanes. Inspect the housing for wear and corrosion.

Gears
Inspect the gear teeth for wear, pits, chips, or rounded corners. Always replace a damaged gear.

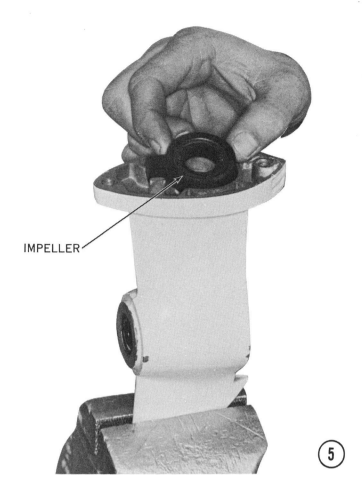

IMPELLER

⑤

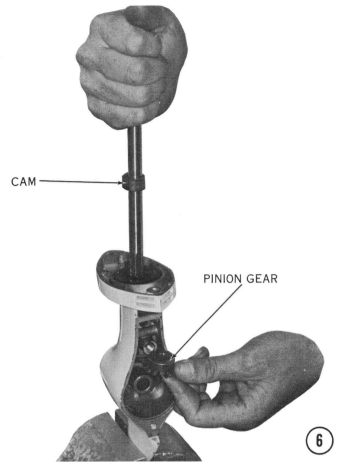

CAM

PINION GEAR

⑥

Shafts

Check the driveshaft and propeller shaft for wear, bend, or twist.

ASSEMBLING

⑤ Install the water pump impeller in the lower unit body. *NOTE: The side marked TOP must face up.*

⑥ Position the pinion gear in the lower cavity, and then insert the driveshaft from the top. *CAUTION: Turn the driveshaft until the cam enters the impeller properly.* The water pump cam is pressed onto the drive-shaft and need not be removed unless damaged. If a new cam is pressed onto the shaft, the measurement from the bottom of the shaft to the bottom of the cam must be exactly 3-1/4″. Slide the pinion gear onto the driveshaft.

⑦ Fill the gear cavity with Texaco 950 Outboard Gear Lubricant, and then slide the propeller shaft, with the bevel gear installed, into the lower unit cavity until the two gears mesh.

⑧ Replace the water pipe in the lower engine casing if the old one is rusted. Secure the pipe with a screw and lockwasher.

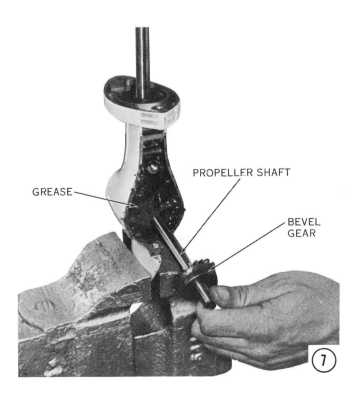

PROPELLER SHAFT

GREASE

BEVEL GEAR

⑦

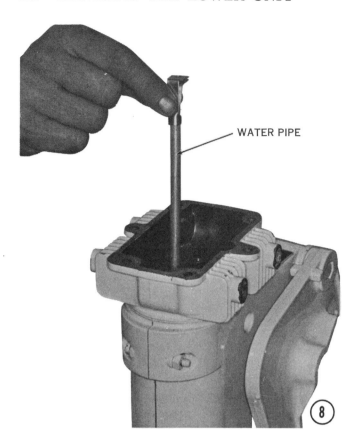

WATER PIPE

(8)

⑨ Place the anti-cavitation plate over the drive-shaft (with the side marked TOP facing up), grease the driveshaft splines, and then slip the lower unit into the lower engine casing. *NOTE: If the engine is in place, it may be necessary to rotate the crankshaft a few degrees to allow the splines to engage the propeller shaft splines. CAUTION: Make sure that the water pipe enters the seal in the anti-cavitation plate properly.* Secure the lower unit to the lower engine casing with the two nuts and lockwashers, torquing them to 135 in.-lbs.

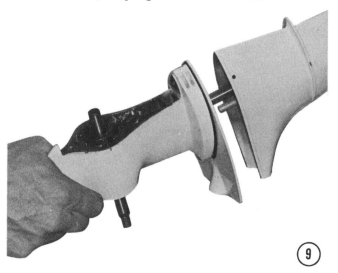

(9)

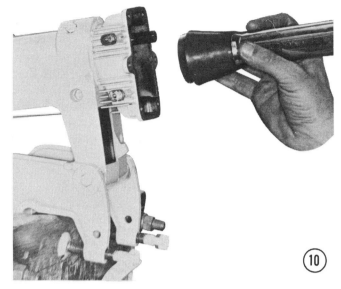

(10)

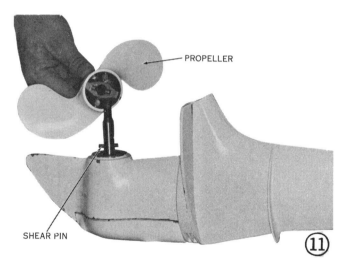

PROPELLER

SHEAR PIN

(11)

⑩ If the engine is not in place, this is a good time to inspect the water pipe to make sure that it has entered the seal properly.

⑪ Install the bearing cap in place, using a new gasket. Install the seal, the shear pin, and the propeller on the propeller shaft. Replace the propeller nut, tighten it with a wrench, and then insert a new cotter key, bending over one of the ends to secure it properly.

TWO-CYLINDER ENGINE

DISASSEMBLY

① Remove the powerhead, as discussed under engine disassembly.

② Drain the oil into a bucket by removing the air vent screw and the drain screw.

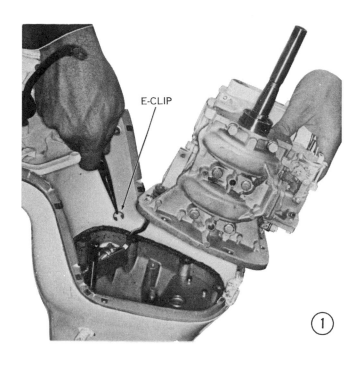

①

③ Pry off the rubber propeller cap, and then remove the cotter key and the thrust washer. Drift out the shear pin, and then slip off the propeller.

④ Take off the two nuts which hold the lower suspension bracket to the engine casing, and then remove the two bolts holding the lower unit in place.

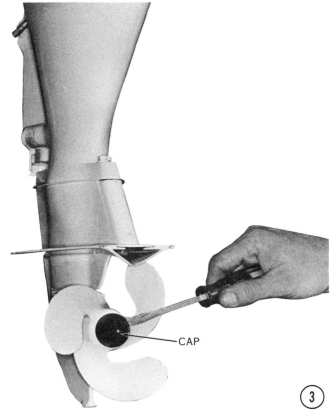

③

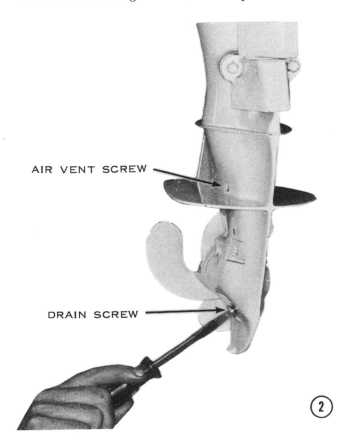

②

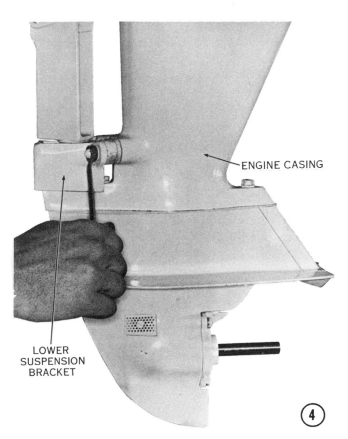

④

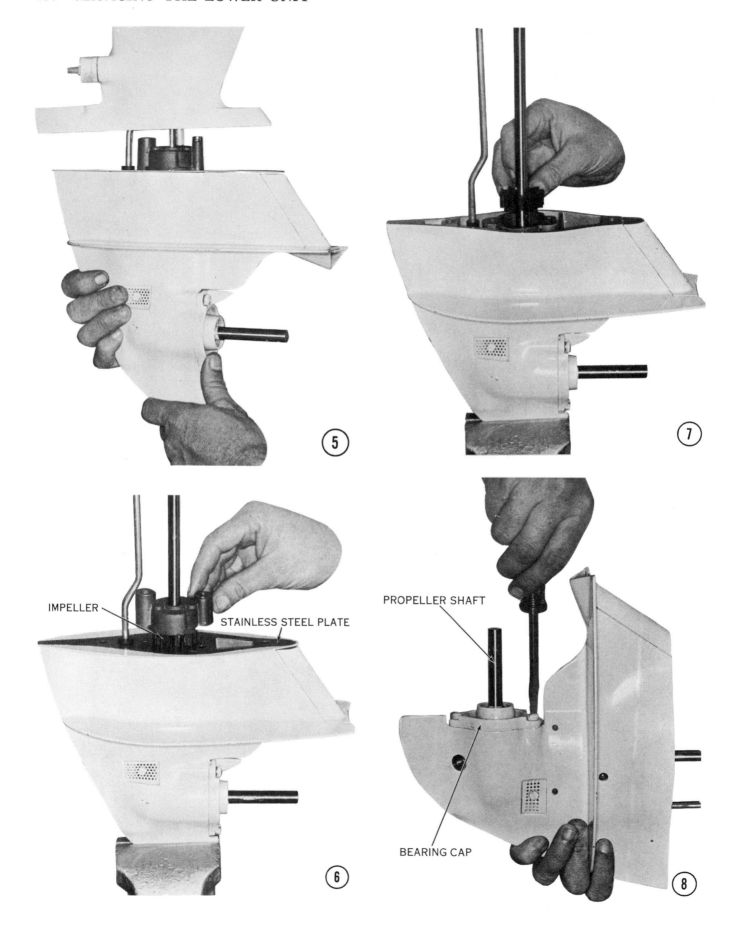

IMPELLER   STAINLESS STEEL PLATE

PROPELLER SHAFT

BEARING CAP

⑤

⑥

⑦

⑧

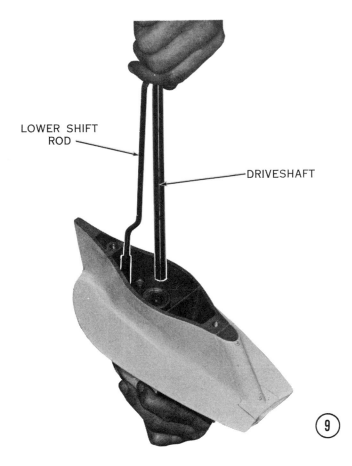

LOWER SHIFT
ROD

DRIVESHAFT

⑨

drive pin from the driveshaft, and then lift off the stainless steel plate.

⑦ Remove the water pump impeller and the drive pin, and then pry off the pump housing.

⑧ Remove the three screws holding the bearing cap in place, and then slide the bearing cap off the propeller shaft. Pull out the propeller shaft with the reverse gear assembly.

⑨ Lift out the driveshaft, and then remove the drive pinion gear from the lower unit cavity. The forward gear now can be taken out of the lower unit cavity. Lift out the lower shift rod. *CAUTION: Hold your hand over the gear cavity to keep from losing the detent and spring, which will pop out.* Remove the detent and spring.

⑩ To disassemble the propeller shaft, remove the clutch dog by compressing the spring in the propeller shaft, and then sliding the clutch dog out of the slot.

⑪ The upper and lower driveshaft bearings can be replaced, if necessary. To remove the bearings, take off the upper driveshaft seal retaining ring and washer. Insert a steel rod with a flat, smooth end through the center of the upper driveshaft bearing. Locate the end of the rod against the upper lip of the lower driveshaft bearing. Tap the end of the rod, working around the circumference of the bushing, until the bushing drops into the lower unit cavity. Use a slide hammer to draw the upper driveshaft bearing out of the body, as shown.

⑤ Pull the lower unit assembly straight down and out of the lower engine casing.

⑥ Take out the two retaining screws, and then pry off the bailing pump housing. Lift the bailing impeller straight up and off the driveshaft. Remove the impeller

CLEANING AND INSPECTING

Clean all parts in solvent and blow dry. A satisfactory inspection cannot be made with dirt masking the

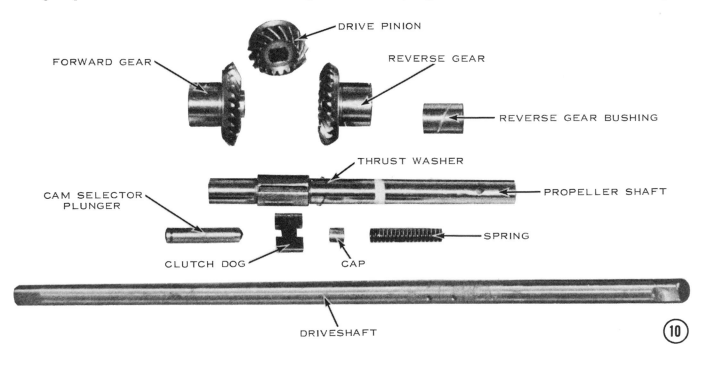

DRIVE PINION

FORWARD GEAR

REVERSE GEAR

REVERSE GEAR BUSHING

THRUST WASHER

CAM SELECTOR
PLUNGER

PROPELLER SHAFT

CLUTCH DOG

CAP

SPRING

DRIVESHAFT

⑩

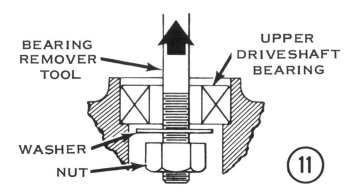

BEARING REMOVER TOOL

UPPER DRIVESHAFT BEARING

WASHER

NUT

(11)

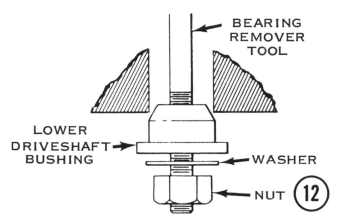

BEARING REMOVER TOOL

LOWER DRIVESHAFT BUSHING

WASHER

NUT (12)

defects. After cleaning, inspect all parts for wear, rust, and other defects.

Seals

Always replace all seals and gaskets.

Water Pump

Check the water pump impeller for wear or broken vanes. Inspect the housing for wear and corrosion.

Gears

Inspect the gear teeth for wear, pits, chips, or rounded corners. Always replace a damaged gear.

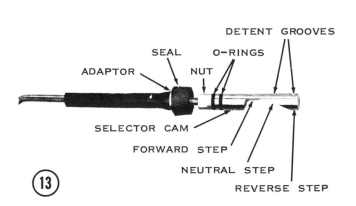

DETENT GROOVES

SEAL O-RINGS

ADAPTOR NUT

SELECTOR CAM

FORWARD STEP

NEUTRAL STEP

REVERSE STEP

(13)

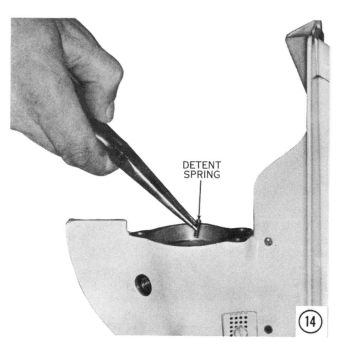

DETENT SPRING

(14)

Shafts

Check the driveshaft and propeller shaft for wear, bend, or twist.

ASSEMBLING

⑫ To install a new lower bearing in the body, use the slide hammer to draw the bearing up into the lower unit body. *CAUTION: Make sure that the bearing is aligned before drawing it up into place.* Press the upper driveshaft bearing into the body, and then install a new driveshaft seal, washer, and retaining ring.

⑬ If the lower shift rod has been disassembled, replace the shift cam spacer tube, adaptor, seal, nut, O-ring seals, and shim on the lower end of the shift rod. Thread the selector cam onto the shift rod until the threads

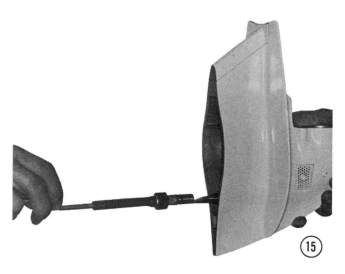

(15)

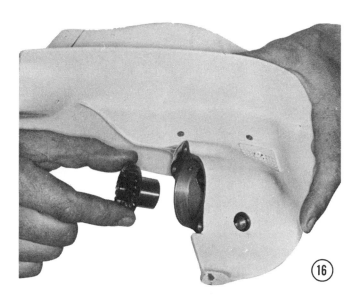

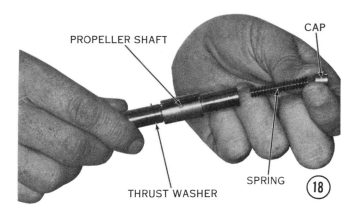

bottom. Reposition the cam as necessary until the face of the cam and the bend in the shift rod face the same direction, and then tighten the nut against the cam.

⑭ Install the detent and the spring into the lower unit cavity.

⑮ Slide the cam selector into its recess in the lower unit until it touches the detent pin, depress the detent pin, and then slide the cam selector all the way into place.

⑯ Install the forward gear (with the pressed-fit bearing sleeve) into the lower unit cavity.

⑰ Install the driveshaft and the pinion gear, sliding the pinion gear onto the end of the driveshaft.

⑱ Assemble the propeller shaft by installing the spring and cap. Note the reverse gear thrust washer on the shaft.

⑲ Clamp the dog clutch securely in a vise, and then compress the spring while you slip the clutch dog into position in the slot of the propeller shaft.

⑳ Slide the cam selector plunger into the propeller shaft until it rests against the clutch dog. *NOTE: The conical end of the cam selector plunger must face out.*

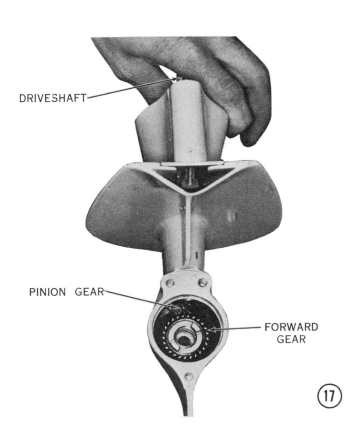

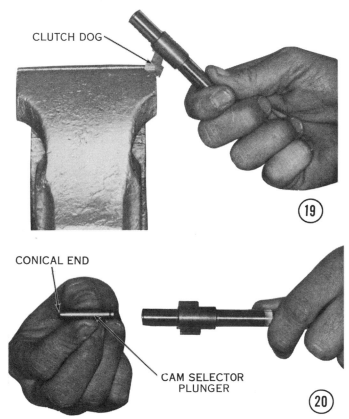

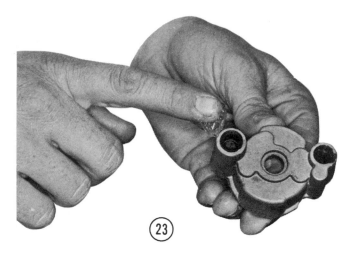

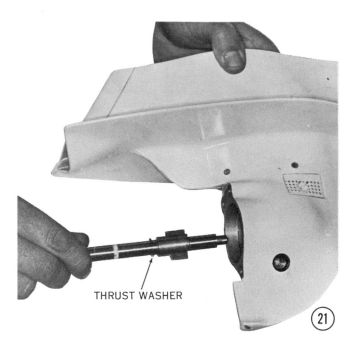

THRUST WASHER

(21)

㉑ Insert the propeller shaft into the lower unit cavity until it enters the forward gear fully. Position the reverse gear thrust washer on the propeller shaft.

㉒ Slide the reverse gear (with the loose bearing sleeve) onto the propeller shaft, and then replace the bearing cap. *CAUTION: Use a new O-ring seal and carefully install the cap to prevent pinching the seal.* Tighten the three retaining screws securely.

㉓ Install new seals, lubricate them with cup grease, and then slide the water pump body over the driveshaft.

㉔ Insert the impeller drive pin and the impeller, making sure that the drive pin properly enters the groove

in the face of the impeller. Lubricate the impeller to keep it from scoring.

㉕ Replace the stainless steel plate. The side stamped TOP must face up. Insert the bailer pump drive pin and the impeller. Lubricate the impeller with oil to keep it from scoring.

㉖ Lubricate the seals on the bailer pump, and then slide it over the driveshaft. Install and tighten the two retaining screws securely.

㉗ Assemble the lower unit on the lower engine casing. Check the water and bailer pipe connections at the pump. *CAUTION: The bailer pipe must fit snugly into the seal of the bailer pump, and the water pipe must protrude through the stainless steel plate and into the water pump seal. CAUTION: Make sure that the*

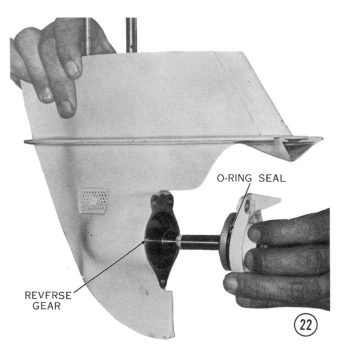

O-RING SEAL

REVERSE
GEAR

(22)

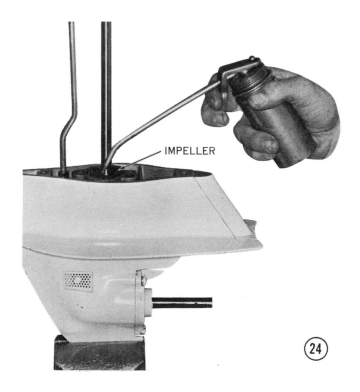

IMPELLER

(24)

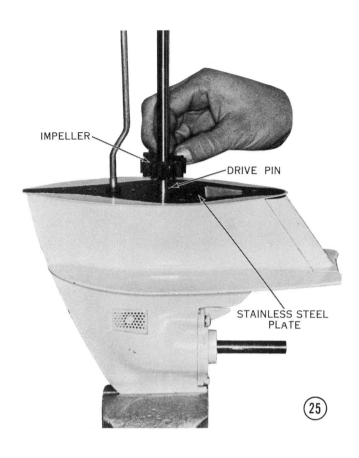

IMPELLER

DRIVE PIN

STAINLESS STEEL PLATE

(25)

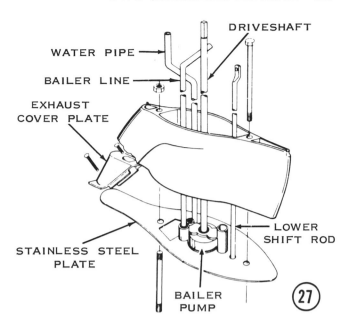

WATER PIPE

DRIVESHAFT

BAILER LINE

EXHAUST COVER PLATE

STAINLESS STEEL PLATE

LOWER SHIFT ROD

BAILER PUMP

(27)

lower water pump seal is in place and that it fits tightly on the water pick-up pipe in the lower unit.

㉘ Tighten the lower unit retaining bolts, and then replace the two lower suspension bracket retaining nuts.

㉙ Install the propeller, holding it in position with the shear pin.

㉚ Slide the thrust washer over the propeller shaft, and then install a new cotter pin. Replace the rubber propeller cap.

㉛ Fill the lower unit with EP 90 Gear Lube. Add the oil through the lower drain hole until the lubricant flows from the vent hole. Replace the drain and vent screws and tighten them securely.

BAILER PUMP HOUSING

(26)

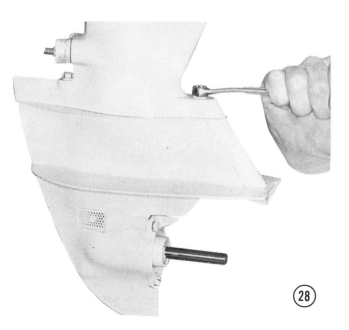

(28)

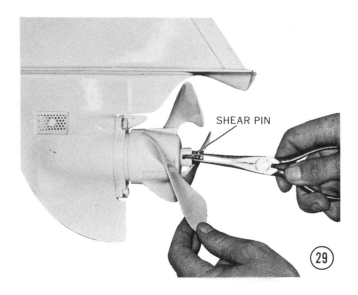

SHEAR PIN

29

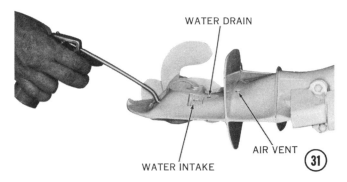

WATER DRAIN

AIR VENT

WATER INTAKE

31

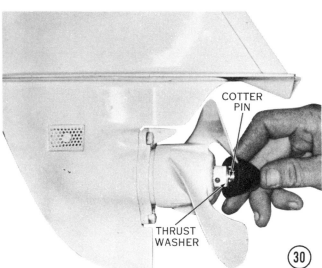

COTTER
PIN

THRUST
WASHER

30

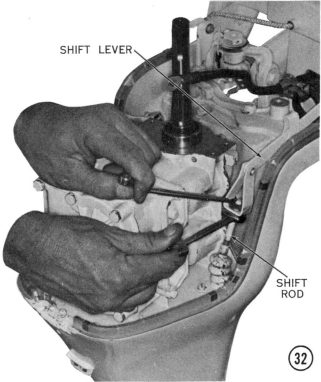

SHIFT LEVER

SHIFT
ROD

32

32 With the shift lever in **NEUTRAL**, the detent pin must drop into the notch in the selector shaft. Move the shift lever on the front panel up and down. You should be able to feel a definite "catch" in **NEUTRAL**.

If the detent position does not align with the **NEUTRAL** position on the front panel, adjust the shift mechanism by turning the upper shift rod as required.

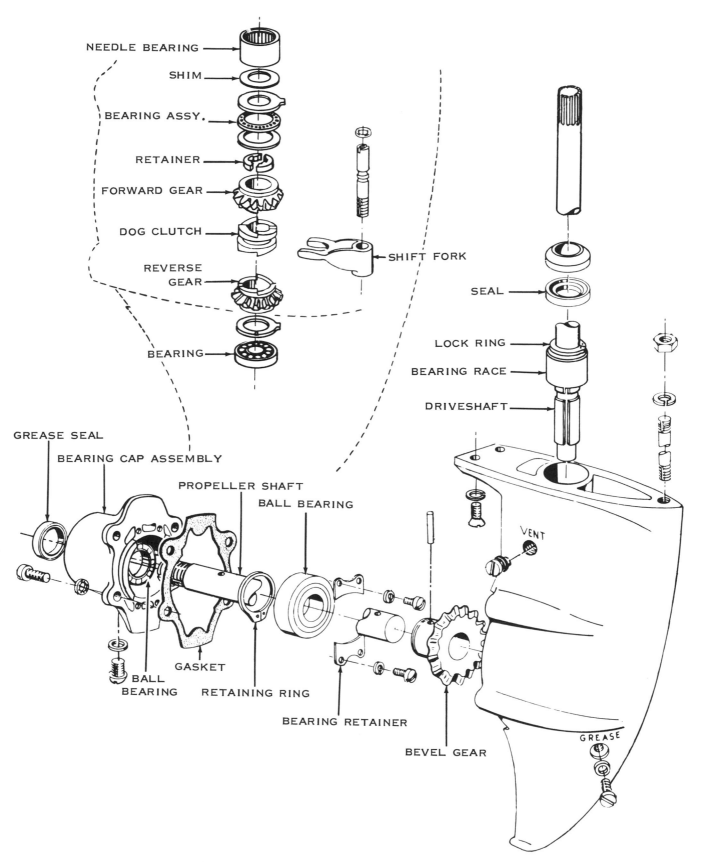

NEEDLE BEARING

SHIM

BEARING ASSY.

RETAINER

FORWARD GEAR

DOG CLUTCH

REVERSE GEAR

BEARING

SHIFT FORK

SEAL

LOCK RING

BEARING RACE

DRIVESHAFT

GREASE SEAL

BEARING CAP ASSEMBLY

PROPELLER SHAFT

BALL BEARING

VENT

BALL BEARING

GASKET

RETAINING RING

BEARING RETAINER

BEVEL GEAR

GREASE

Exploded view of the lower unit of the 12 and 14 Hp engines.

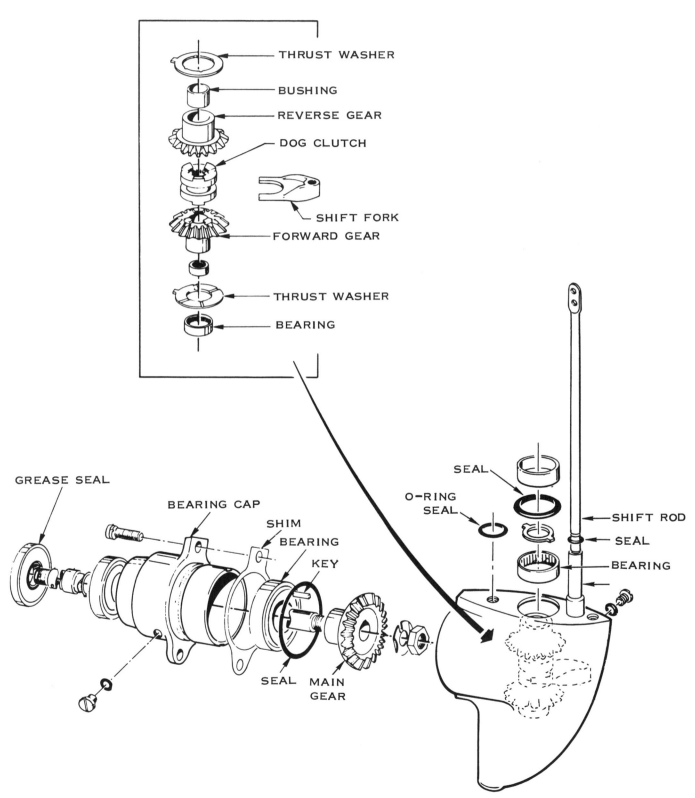

THRUST WASHER

BUSHING

REVERSE GEAR

DOG CLUTCH

SHIFT FORK

FORWARD GEAR

THRUST WASHER

BEARING

GREASE SEAL

BEARING CAP

SHIM

BEARING

KEY

SEAL

MAIN
GEAR

SEAL

O-RING
SEAL

SHIFT ROD

SEAL

BEARING

Exploded view of the lower unit of the 25 and 28 Hp engines.

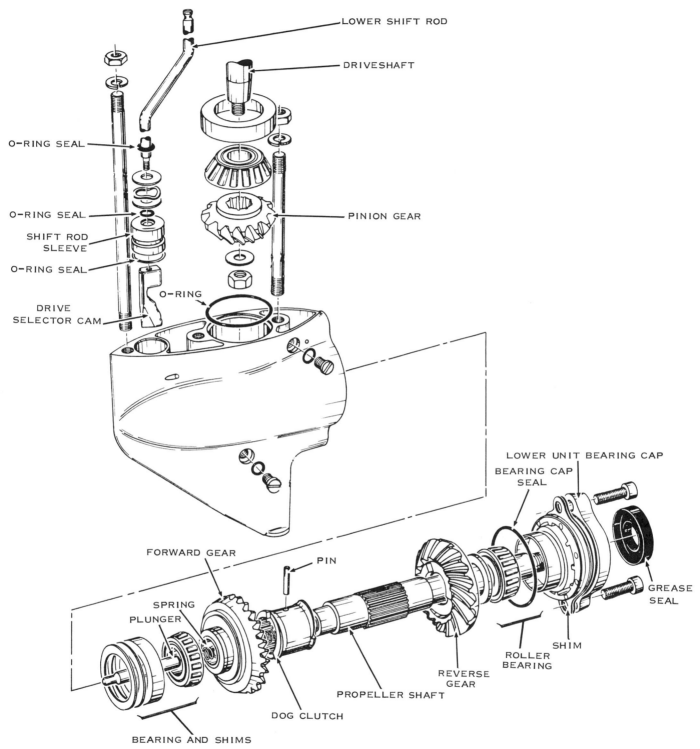

LOWER SHIFT ROD

DRIVESHAFT

O-RING SEAL

O-RING SEAL

SHIFT ROD
SLEEVE

O-RING SEAL

PINION GEAR

O-RING

DRIVE
SELECTOR CAM

LOWER UNIT BEARING CAP

BEARING CAP
SEAL

GREASE
SEAL

FORWARD GEAR

PIN

SPRING

PLUNGER

SHIM

ROLLER
BEARING

REVERSE
GEAR

PROPELLER SHAFT

DOG CLUTCH

BEARING AND SHIMS

Exploded view of the lower unit used on the 40, 43, 45, 60, and 75 Hp engines.

7
ELECTRICAL SYSTEM SERVICE

Some of the larger engines are equipped with an electric cranking motor. Because of the large electrical drain, it is necessary to connect a 12-volt storage battery to supply the current. These models have an alternator mounted under the flywheel to charge the battery while the engine is cruising.

The 7.5 and 9 Hp engines are optionally equipped with a combination starter-generator, which also requires an external battery. The starter-generator functions as a generator when the engine is operating at cruising speed.

CRANKING MOTORS

Two types of cranking motors have been used: Delco-Remy and Prestolite. The Delco-Remy cranking motor was used through early 1965. Since then, the Prestolite has been used.

OVERHAULING A DELCO-REMY CRANKING MOTOR

DISASSEMBLING

Remove the through-bolts, which will release the

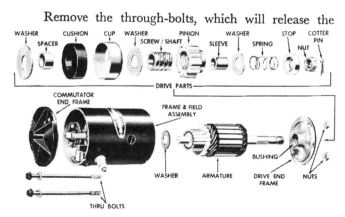

Exploded view of the Delco-Remy cranking motor.

commutator end frame. Slide the armature and drive-end frame from the field housing. To disassemble the drive, slide a half-inch pipe coupling onto the shaft so that the end of the coupling butts against the edge of the pinion stop collar.

Tap the end of the coupling to drive the stop collar toward the armature in order to release the snap ring. Remove the snap ring from the groove in the shaft, and then take off the drive, spring, and spacer.

Some Delco-Remy cranking motors have a Bendix drive, which is secured to the armature shaft with a roll pin. To remove this type, raise the pinion assembly to expose the hole in the screw shaft. Rotate the screw shaft to expose the roll pin, and then use a punch to drive it out and to release the drive from the shaft.

CLEANING AND INSPECTING

The field and the brush assembly can be checked for an open or grounded circuit by means of a test lamp. Place one test lamp probe on the insulated terminal and the other probe on the metal frame. The lamp must not light, or the part is shorted to ground.

The armature should be checked for open circuits, short circuits, and ground. This is accomplished best on a growler. Open-circuited cranking motor armatures often can be soldered if the connections are melted out at the commutator. *CAUTION: Use only rosin flux. Acid-type flux will cause corrosion.*

If the commutator is burned or out-of-round, it is necessary to true it in a lathe, and then undercut the mica to about 1/32″.

The drive-end bronze bushing should be replaced during each overhaul. If the commutator end bushing is worn, it is necessary to replace the end frame assembly.

To replace the insulated brushes, first cut off the old brush lead at the point where it is attached to the field coils. Solder the lead from the new brush to the back side of the coil so that excess solder cannot rub against the armature. *CAUTION: Do not overheat the flexible leads because the solder will flow into the braid and make the lead stiff.*

The ground brushes can be removed by drilling out the rivets. The new brushes come with a new screw, washer, and nut. After tightening the nut, peen the screw so that the nut cannot vibrate loose during operation.

ASSEMBLING

Assemble the Delco-Remy drive to the armature shaft as follows: Lubricate the splined portion of the shaft with SAE 30 oil. Install the two collars on the shaft, with the countersunk side toward the end frame. Position the drive return spring on the shaft, with the smaller diameter toward the end frame. Install a turn of the small end of the spring into the groove of the shaft, next to the end frame. Hook the end of the spring into the hole at the bottom of the groove. *CAUTION: Be careful not to distort the spring.*

Hold the spring out of the way while assembling the drive. Wind up the free end of the spring 3/4 turn, and then hook it into the nearest hole in the drive plate. Slide the pinion stop collar onto the shaft, with its cupped surface facing away from the drive. Install the snap ring in the groove, and then squeeze the ring with pliers to force it into the groove properly.

Position the pinion stop collar next to the snap ring, and then temporarily install a washer next to the other side of the snap ring. Use two pairs of pliers to grip the stop collar and washer in order to force it over the snap ring, as shown. *CAUTION: The stop collar must rotate freely when assembled.* Rotate the drive against the pinion stop and release any spring turns which may be overlapping other turns. *NOTE: When the spring is properly assembled, the drive should return snappily from the engaged position.*

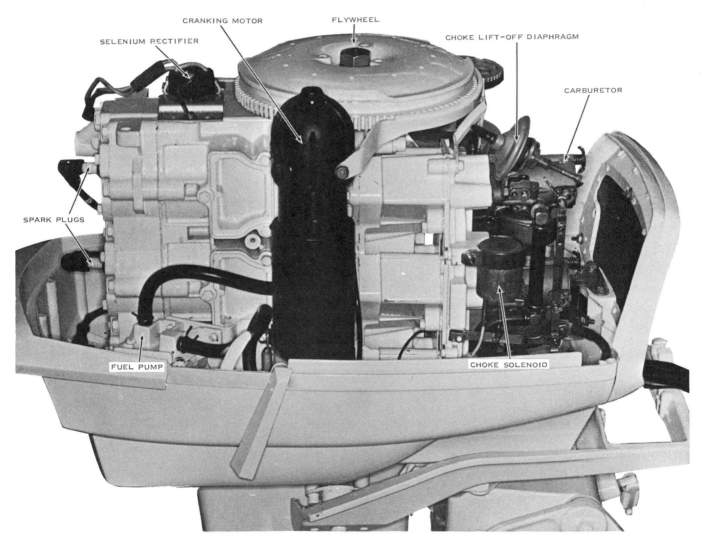

Side view of the powerplant of the 75 Hp engine.

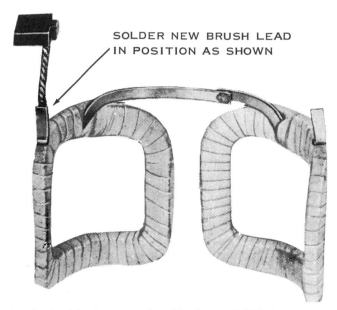

SOLDER NEW BRUSH LEAD IN POSITION AS SHOWN

The insulated brushes have to be soldered to the field leads, as shown.

Position the thrust washer on the commutator end of the armature, and then slide the assembly into the field frame, being careful not to damage the commutator or the brushes. Replace the commutator end frame and install the through-bolts. Brush liquid neoprene on the cranking motor wherever the original seal has been broken. This will seal the unit against moisture.

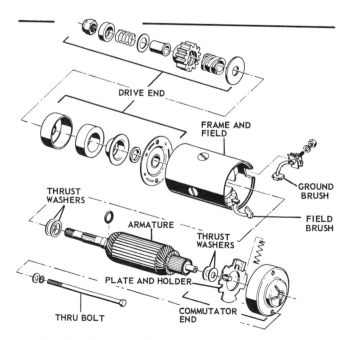

Exploded view of the Prestolite cranking motor used since 1965.

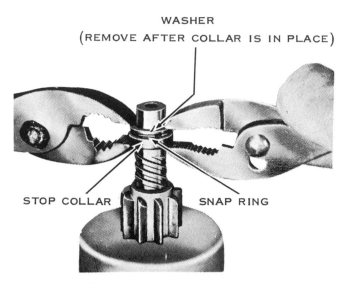

WASHER (REMOVE AFTER COLLAR IS IN PLACE)

STOP COLLAR   SNAP RING

Force the stop collar into position with two pairs of pliers and a washer which is temporarily positioned above the snap ring.

OVERHAULING A PRESTO-LITE CRANKING MOTOR

DISASSEMBLING

To disassemble the cranking motor, remove the motor and bracket assembly from the engine, and then take out the two through-bolts. To disassemble the drive end, remove the locknut, and then slide the parts from the armature shaft. *CAUTION: Slide a socket into the commutator end plate to keep the brushes from dropping out of the holders.* Note the number of thrust washers for assembly purposes.

CLEANING AND INSPECTING

The field and the brush assembly can be checked for an open or grounded circuit by means of a test lamp. Place one test lamp probe on the insulated terminal and the other probe on the metal frame. The lamp must not light, or the part is shorted to ground.

The armature should be checked for open circuits, short circuits, and ground. This is accomplished best on a growler. Open-circuited cranking motor armatures often can be soldered if the connections are melted out at the commutator. *CAUTION: Use only rosin flux. Acid-type flux will cause corrosion.*

If the commutator is burned or out-of-round, it is necessary to true it in a lathe, and then undercut the mica to about 1/32".

The drive-end bronze bushing should be replaced at each overhaul. If the commutator end bushing is worn, it is necessary to replace the end frame assembly.

To replace the field brush, cut the lead from the ground stud and use rosin flux to solder the lead to the field coil post. *CAUTION: Make sure that the lead comes off the proper side of the post so that the brush will reach the brush holder. CAUTION: Don't overheat the lead, as the solder will run into the braid and stiffen the lead.*

To replace the ground brush, first remove the old brush and then attach the new assembly to the frame, with the screw, washer, and nut included with the package. Peen the screw to keep the assembly from loosening.

ASSEMBLING

Lubricate the splined portion of the armature with Lubriplate No. 630—AA, and then slide the drive onto the armature shaft. Replace the locknut. Slide the armature into the field frame, replace the thrust washers, and then insert the brushes into their holders. *CAUTION: Be careful not to twist the brush springs out of shape.* Position the brush plate and holder over the end of the shaft, and then lift the brushes over the commutator. Check to see that the brushes are free in their holders and seat properly against the commutator.

Replace the head plate. *NOTE: The guide holes in the plate match locating pins on the head to insure align-* ment. Insert and tighten the through-bolts to 40 in.-lbs. Check the armature end play, which must be a minimum of 0.005″. If there is insufficient end play, disassemble the commutator end plate and remove one of the washers. *NOTE: Excessive end play is not important.* Brush liquid neoprene on the cranking motor wherever the original seal has been broken. This will seal the unit against moisture.

STARTER-GENERATOR

7.5 & 9 HP ENGINES

The accompanying circuit diagrams show the flow of current under varying circumstances.

Normal Starting

When the battery is connected and the START button is depressed, the solenoid is activated, allowing current to flow to the starter-generator, which acts as a starter and cranks the engine. When the engine starts, it turns the armature, and the unit functions as a generator.

Charging

Because of the residual magnetism in the fields, the armature, which is being turned by the crankshaft, functions as a generator. A diode in the circuit prevents current from passing from the battery to the starter-generator, but permits rectified current from the generator to pass through and charge the battery.

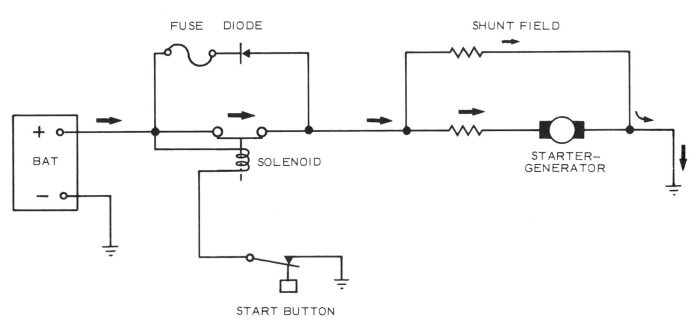

Schematic wiring diagram of the starter-generator when the START button is depressed. The armature cranks the engine.

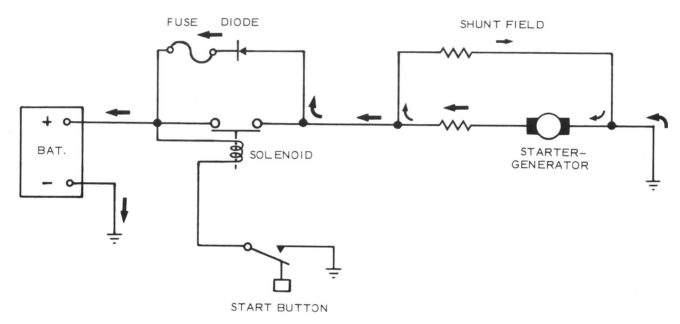

At cruising speed, the unit becomes a generator to charge the battery.

Start Button Depressed Accidentally

If the START button is depressed while the engine is running at idle speed, the solenoid will be activated and allow current to flow to the starter-generator. Because this voltage is greater than that being generated at idle, the starter-generator will act as a starter, and the speed of the engine will increase. The operator will be come aware of the increased speed and release the START button. No damage to the unit will result.

If the START button is depressed while the engine is running at cruising speed, the starter-generator will be acting as a generator. The solenoid will be activated, allowing current to flow directly from the starter-generator to the battery, bypassing the diode. This direct path

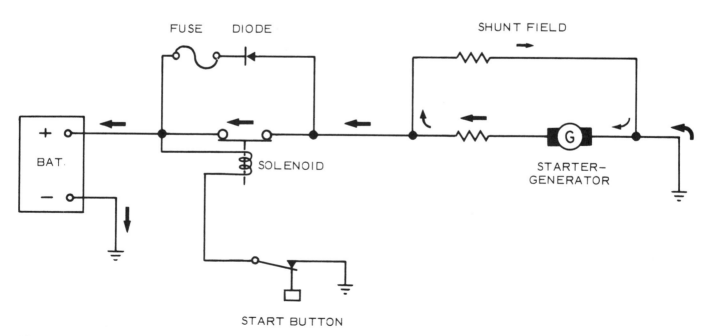

If the START button is depressed accidentally when the engine is running at cruising speed, the diode is shorted out of the circuit so that the battery receives unrectified current. This will not damage the battery if the START button is released quickly.

will boost the charging rate, but the current drain of the solenoid is large enough to overcome this added current so that an actual discharge results. No electrical damage to the parts of the system will result, but this practice is not recommended.

If the engine is to be run without a battery, disable the generator by pulling out the brushes enough for them to be caught by the brush springs. *CAUTION: If the engine is operated without a battery and the generator is not disabled, the charging voltage will rise enough to damage the generator.*

STARTER-GENERATOR TROUBLESHOOTING

BATTERY SERVICE

Check the state of battery charge with a hydrometer. Take a reading from each cell; the minimum should be 1.040. Recharge or replace the battery, if it is dead. If the electrolyte level is too low, add distilled water. *CAUTION: It takes 24 hours for the water to mix with the electrolyte; therefore, a hydrometer reading, immediately after adding water, will be meaningless.*

Make sure that the battery terminals are clean, tight, and free from corrosion and that the wires are not damaged. Use a wire brush to remove any corrosion. In-

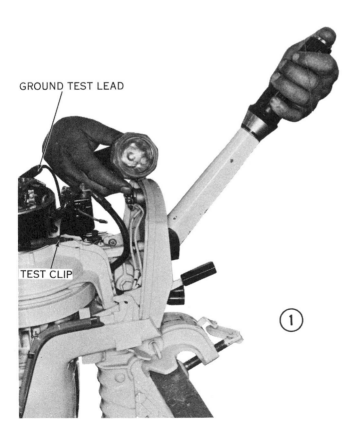

GROUND TEST LEAD

TEST CLIP

①

②

spect the battery lead connections at the front panel to be sure that they are free from corrosion and that they are clean and fit together tightly. A tighter fit may be obtained by spreading the ends of the male connectors with a screwdriver. Inspect the battery lead connections at the solenoid and at the ground terminal to make sure that they are not damaged and that the connections are tight. Replace any damaged terminal and tighten loose connections.

ELECTRICAL TESTS

CAUTION: Always disconnect the battery leads at the front panel before opening the hood. This is to avoid sparks that might start a fire and to prevent accidental shorts that could damage expensive test equipment.

① Use a self-powered test lamp to test the START button. Do this by disconnecting the battery leads at the front panel and then opening the hood. Disconnect the center (white) lead connector from the solenoid to the START button (at the solenoid), and then connect one test lamp clip to this lead. Connect the other test lamp clip to any good ground. Press the START button; if the test lamp lights, the circuit is good. If the test lamp does not light or if the test lamp lights without depression of the START button, the circuit is open or shorted.

② To service the START button, remove the two Allen-headed setscrews from the twist-grip handle, and then remove the switch retainer and the START button assembly. *CAUTION: Don't pull on or jerk the switch, or you will damage the terminal or wire.*

③ Remove the terminal screw, and then separate the wire assembly, washers, switch retainer, spring, and button. Inspect the wire assembly for insulation damage and the terminal for cracks. Wrap damaged insulation with tape. Replace the terminal if it is damaged. Inspect the START button, switch retainer, spring, and terminal screw for damage. Replace any part that is doubtful. Make sure that the washers and the terminal screw are free from corrosion. Inspect the wire between the handle and the handle mount, making sure that the insulation is not damaged and that the connections are tight. If

③

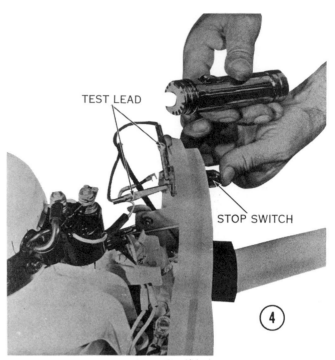

TEST LEAD

STOP SWITCH

④

the wire needs to be replaced, drive out the roll pin at the geared joint of the handle because the terminal on the end of the wire will not pass this restriction. *NOTE: Drive the roll pin out partially. It is not necessary to take it out entirely.* Assemble the switch, making sure that the two connections between the switch and the wires are secure, and then replace the two setscrews.

④ The stop switch can be tested with a self-powered test lamp. First, test the stop switch for an open or short circuit. To do this, disconnect the battery leads from the front panel and then open the hood. Disconnect one lead from the stop switch terminal. Connect one test lead to either of the two stop switch terminals and the other test lead to the remaining terminal. Press the button, and

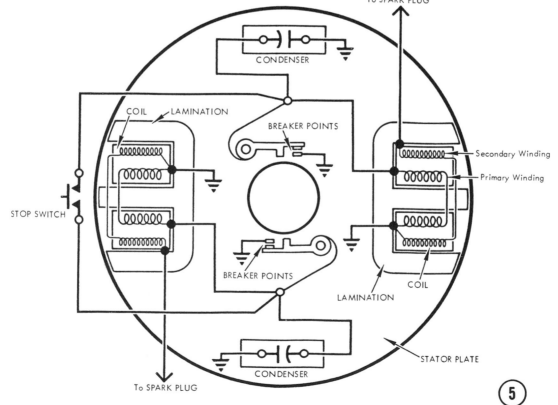

To SPARK PLUG

CONDENSER

COIL   LAMINATION

BREAKER POINTS

Secondary Winding

Primary Winding

STOP SWITCH

BREAKER POINTS

LAMINATION

COIL

STATOR PLATE

To SPARK PLUG

CONDENSER

⑤

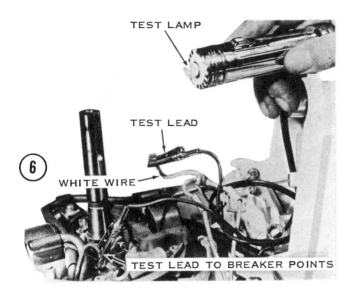

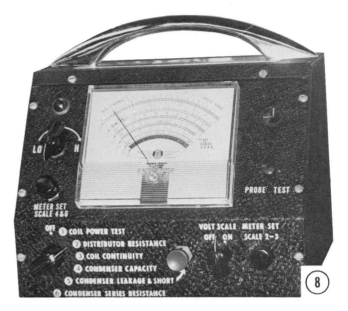

the test lamp should light. If it doesn't, replace the switch.

⑤ The stop switch is connected in parallel with both sets of breaker points. This type of circuit grounds out the open set of breaker points through the set which is closed.

⑥ To test the wiring of this circuit, the starter-generator, manual starter housing, and the flywheel must be removed to gain access to the wires, after which they can be checked with a self-powered test lamp in the usual manner. An ohmmeter can be used to check the circuit without removing the flywheel, as discussed in Step ⑦.

⑦ If an ohmmeter is available, the circuit can be tested without removing the flywheel by measuring the resistance between each switch lead and ground. To

check the wiring with an ohmmeter, connect one of the ohmmeter test leads to one switch wire and the other to a good ground. Turn the flywheel and the meter should read the resistance of the primary winding of the magneto when the breaker points are *open*.

⑧ The pointer should return to the left side of the scale when the flywheel is turned enough to close the set of breaker points. *CAUTION: The reading will not be zero because of the resistance between the contact point surfaces.* Repeat the test with the other wire from the stop switch. If there is zero resistance between either wire and ground when the flywheel is turned (breaker points opening and closing), then the wire is shorted to ground. If the meter shows a full-scale deflection when the flywheel is turned, then the wire is open circuited. If necessary, replace the wire or the stop switch.

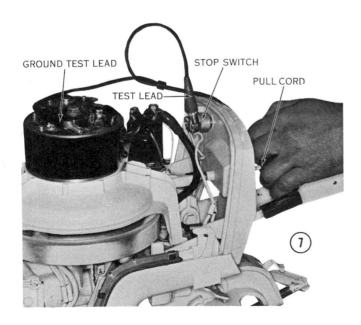

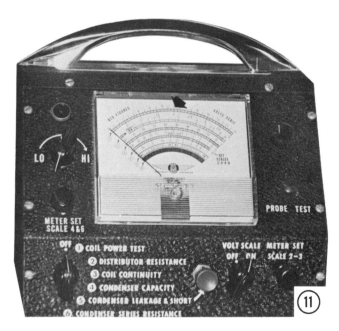

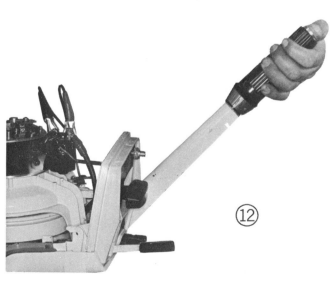

STARTER-GENERATOR SERVICE

Output Test

⑨ An ammeter must be connected into the charging circuit to test the output of the generator. Two types of test meters are available: an induction type and a shunt type. The induction type meter shown can be placed against the main wire, and it will register the amount of current that the wire is carrying. *NOTE: This type of test meter does not have to be connected into the circuit.*

⑩ The shunt type of meter must be connected into the circuit as follows: Disconnect the small red generator lead underneath the battery lead on the solenoid terminal, farthest from the starter-generator. Connect the positive (+) ammeter lead to the disconnected generator lead. Connect the negative (−) ammeter lead to the outside solenoid terminal, and then reconnect the battery lead. Mount the engine in a test tank, and then start it. The ammeter should register 3–8 amperes at 4,200–5,500 rpm. If the output is less than specifications, the starter-generator will have to be disassembled for further testing.

Solenoid Output Test

⑪ Disconnect the battery leads at the front panel, and then open the hood. Use a Merc-O-Tronic tester by turning the FUNCTION SWITCH to the OFF position and the VOLTS SCALE knob to the ON position. Connect the small red test lead to the solenoid terminal farthest from the starter-generator. Connect the small black test lead to the solenoid terminal closest to the starter-generator. Reconnect the battery leads at the front panel. The meter should now read 12 volts.

⑫ Press the START button, and the engine should turn (be cranked). The meter pointer should indicate approximately zero volts. If the meter pointer indicates less than 12 volts, check the condition of the battery and the wiring terminals. If the meter pointer indicates a significant voltage while the START button is depressed, replace the solenoid because the contacts are corroded. *NOTE: The voltage drop across the contacts is registering on the meter as voltage.*

Solenoid Energizing Test

⑬ Disconnect the battery leads to the front panel, and then open the hood. Disconnect both leads from the terminal post which is farthest from the starter-generator. *NOTE: The farthest solenoid terminal post must be completely bare.* Connect the black test lead of an ohmmeter to the bare terminal of the solenoid and the red test lead to the other terminal. Reconnect the battery leads at the front panel. Make contact between the solenoid lead and

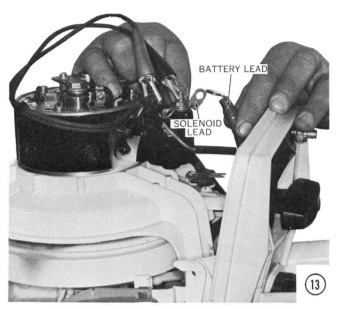

BATTERY LEAD

SOLENOID LEAD

⑬

Using an ohmmeter, connect the small black test lead to the solenoid terminal farthest from the starter-generator, and then touch the small red test lead to the diode plate. The meter pointer will either move across the scale or it won't move at all, depending on which way the test leads are connected. If the meter pointer does not move across the scale, it indicates that current is not flowing through the diode. Reverse the test leads, and the meter pointer should deflect approximately full scale. If the meter pointer does not deflect when the test leads are reversed, or if the meter pointer deflects fully with the test leads in both positions, replace the diode assembly. The diode is protected by a fuse, which will burn out if the battery is connected in reverse. *CAUTION: Don't use a substitute for the fuse, or you will cause damage to the generator.*

the red battery lead that comes from the front panel, and then have a helper press the START button on the handle to complete the solenoid circuit. The meter should read zero resistance if the contact points are good.

STARTER-GENERATOR, R&R

⑮ Disconnect the battery leads at the front panel, the red-sleeved battery lead at the solenoid terminal farthest from the starter-generator, and the center white start button lead connector. Lift off the cover. Remove

Diode Test
⑭ Disconnect the battery at the front panel, and then open the hood. Remove the starter-generator cover.

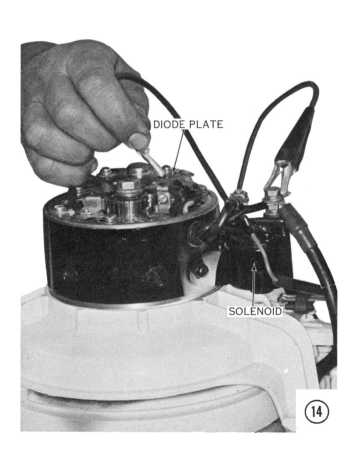

DIODE PLATE

SOLENOID

⑭

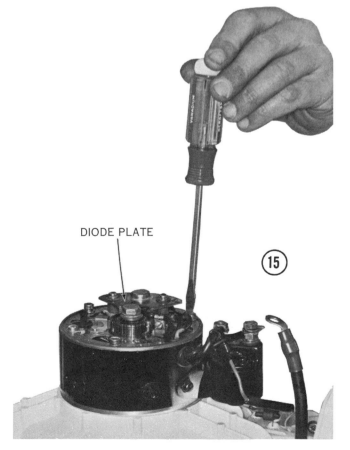

DIODE PLATE

⑮

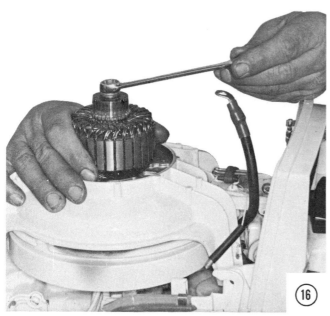

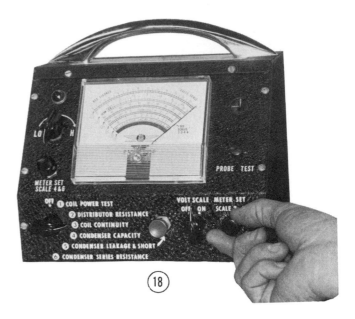

the three hold-down screws, and then lift the stator assembly straight off the armature. Remove the two diode assembly mounting screws, and then unsolder the lead from the solenoid as close to the diode plate as possible. Unsolder the lead to the fields as close to the diode tip as possible, and then remove the diode assembly and the two insulators. *CAUTION: Hold a wet rag around the*

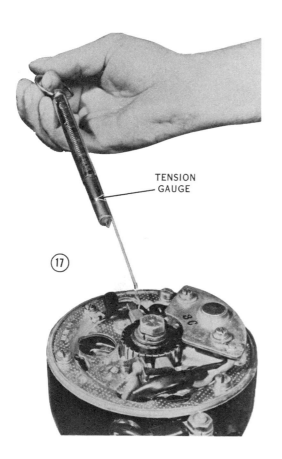

TENSION GAUGE

diode base to keep the heat away from the diode, which is easily destroyed by heat. Remove the two solenoid-mounting screws, disconnect the remaining connections, and then remove the solenoid.

⑯ Remove the armature retaining bolt, and then lift off the armature. If the armature is difficult to remove, place a 1/4" x 1-1/4" long piece of drill rod in the bolt hole. Screw in a 3/8" x 24" bolt to force the armature off the crankshaft. Remove the Woodruff key and the spacer. *CAUTION: Don't pry against the bottom of the armature to remove it, or you will damage the windings.*

CLEANING AND INSPECTING

⑰ Clean all parts in solvent and wipe dry. *CAUTION: Don't use compressed air to dry the parts and don't soak the armature or fields in solvent, or you will damage the insulation.* Check the brushes, which should be replaced if they measure less than 1/2" in length. Brush spring tension should be 12 oz.

Brush Holders and Field Windings

⑱ To test the field windings, remove the screw attaching the shunt field lead to the stator plate, and then position the lead so that it doesn't make contact with the plate. Use an ohmmeter or the Merc-O-Tronic tester with the selector switch turned to the No. 3 position. With the test leads touching, adjust the meter until the pointer lines up with the SET line.

⑲ Touch one test lead to the insulated brush and the other test lead to a good ground on the stator assembly. There must be no deflection of the meter pointer. If there is a partial or full-scale deflection of the meter

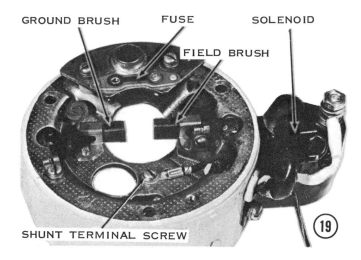

GROUND BRUSH   FUSE   SOLENOID

FIELD BRUSH

SHUNT TERMINAL SCREW

⑲

㉑

pointer, the field windings are shorted, which requires replacement of the entire stator assembly. Touch the disconnected shunt field lead to the stator plate, and the meter pointer should deflect approximately full scale, indicating continuity through the shunt field.

Armature

⑳ Test the armature for shorted windings on a growler. Slowly rotate the armature with one hand while holding a hacksaw blade over the laminations. If an armature coil is shorted, the hacksaw blade will vibrate, meaning that the armature should be replaced.

㉑ Test the armature for ground by using an ohmmeter or the Merc-O-Tronic tester with the selector switch in the No. 3 position. Touch one test lead to the commutator and the other to the armature core. Any movement of the meter pointer indicates that the armature is grounded and must be replaced. If the commuta-

tor is burned, the armature should be set up in a lathe and a very light cut taken from the surface of the commutator. After truing the commutator, undercut the mica to a depth of 0.020″–0.030″.

Diodes

㉒ The diode can be tested with an ohmmeter or the Merc-O-Tronic tester with the selector switch in the No. 3 position. There must be an open circuit when the test leads are connected to each terminal of the diode and almost full-scale deflection of the meter pointer when the test leads are reversed.

ASSEMBLING

㉓ Replace the spacer and the Woodruff key. Install the armature and torque the retaining bolt to 225 in.-lbs.

㉔ Replace the stator assembly. Hold the brushes in the retracted position so that they can pass over the commutator. Secure the assembly with the three through-bolts.

⑳

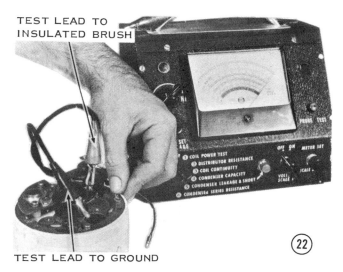

TEST LEAD TO INSULATED BRUSH

TEST LEAD TO GROUND

㉒

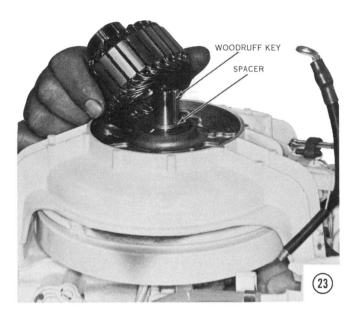

WOODRUFF KEY

SPACER

㉓

㉕ Connect the red-sleeved battery lead to the solenoid terminal farthest from the starter-generator. Connect the center white start button lead at the quick-disconnect fitting. Pull the rubber insulating sleeve over the connection. Replace the cover.

ALTERNATOR

All engines with an electric cranking motor are equipped with an alternator that generates 4–6 amperes for the two-cylinder models and 10–12 amperes for the 75 Hp engine at 5,000 rpm.

㉔

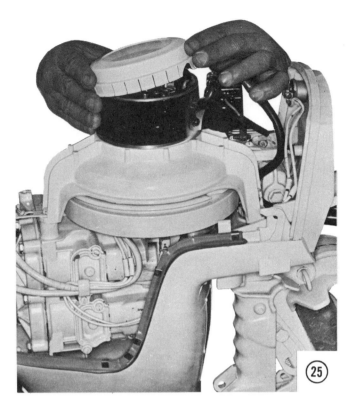

㉕

The alternator coils are mounted on a laminated iron core beneath the flywheel. Current is induced in the coils by the rotating magnets which are imbedded in the flywheel. This AC current is passed through a selenium rectifier which changes the alternating current into direct current to charge the battery.

ALTERNATOR TESTS

The coils can be checked for continuity and ground with any self-powered test lamp or an ohmmeter. Dis-

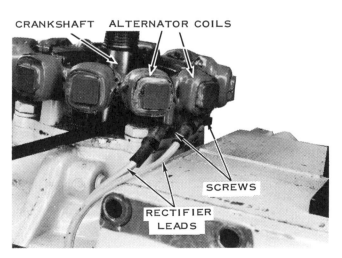

CRANKSHAFT   ALTERNATOR COILS

SCREWS

RECTIFIER LEADS

The alternator coils are positioned under the flywheel.

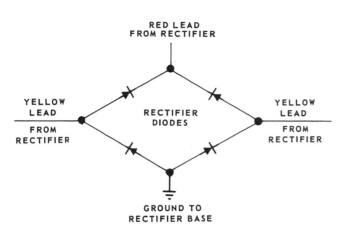

RED LEAD
FROM RECTIFIER

YELLOW
LEAD
FROM
RECTIFIER

RECTIFIER
DIODES

YELLOW
LEAD
FROM
RECTIFIER

GROUND TO
RECTIFIER BASE

The rectifier for the larger engines is composed of four diodes hooked up in a bridge-type circuit. It is necessary to make four separate tests to check each of the four diodes.

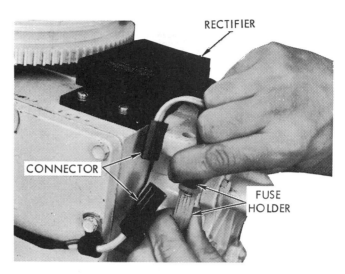

RECTIFIER

CONNECTOR

FUSE
HOLDER

The generating circuit of the 75 Hp engine is fused with an AGC 14 ampere fuse. If the fuse blows out, be sure to check the charging system for the defect which caused the fuse failure.

connect the alternator leads, and then attach the test clips to each coil wire. The test lamp should light to indicate continuity. Connect one test lead to ground and the other to either of the alternator leads. There must be no connection to ground.

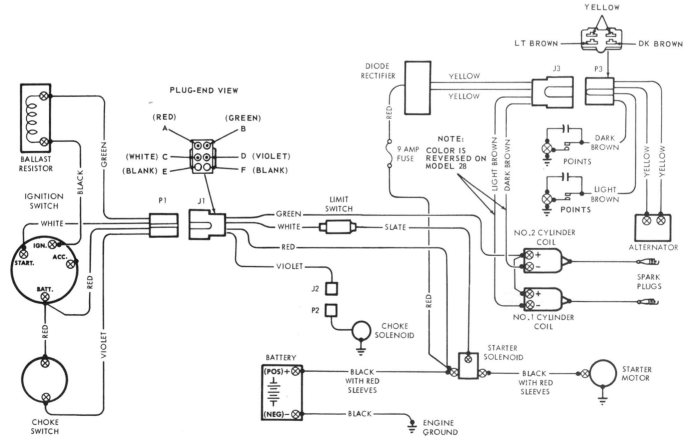

Schematic wiring diagram for the 28 and 45 Hp engines.

SELENIUM RECTIFIER TESTS

Disconnect the red wire to the selenium rectifier at the fuse junction. Using an ohmmeter, connect the small red test lead to the disconnected red lead from the rectifier and the other small black test lead to the metallic case of the rectifier. The meter pointer will not move, or it will deflect to almost a full-scale reading, depending on how you have the test leads connected. Reverse the test leads and, if the rectifier is good, the meter action should be the reverse of the first test. If the meter pointer did not move in the first test, then it should indicate a reading in the second test. If the meter pointer showed a reading in the first test, then it shouldn't move in the second test.

If the meter pointer does not deflect when the test leads are reversed, or if the meter pointer deflects fully with the test leads in both positions, replace the selenium rectifier.

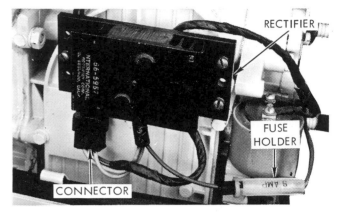

A 9-ampere fuse is used in the 14 and 28 Hp engine generating systems.

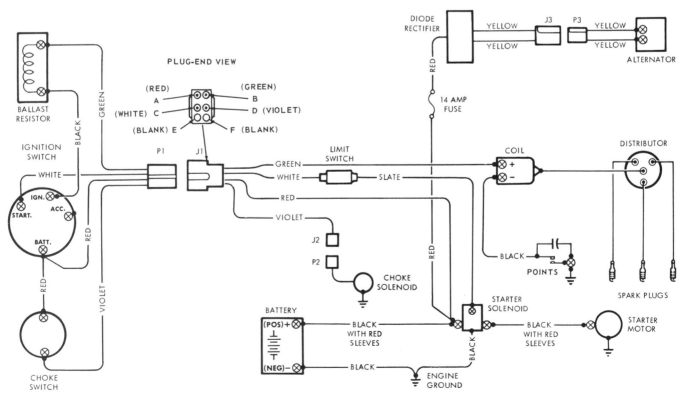

Schematic wiring diagram for the 75 Hp engine.